BELIEF *beyond* PAIN

Jenny Francis was born of Scottish parents but largely reared in other parts of the United Kingdom. She has had considerable social work experience in both hospital and voluntary agencies, maintaining a keen interest in how people adapt to illness and deal with pain in particular, her own experience lending credibility and compassion. Her extensive involvement in Christian counselling and lay training agencies included six years as a therapist with Care and Counsel and two years as Director of Christian Caring in Cambridge. Currently she works with volunteers from local bereavement projects and a local hospice, while continuing as a therapist and as a consultant for other counsellors. She has been married to David, whom she met at university, since 1968.

JENNY FRANCIS

BELIEF *beyond* PAIN

TRIANGLE

First published 1992

SPCK
Holy Trinity Church
Marylebone Road
London NW1 4DU

British Library Cataloguing in Publication Data
A catalogue record for this book is available from the British Library.
ISBN 0-281-04604-2

Typeset by Inforum Typesetting, Portsmouth
Printed in Great Britain by
BPCC Hazells Ltd
Member of BPCC Ltd

Contents

To David,
a husband without price
who shares it all.

'Love bade me welcome:'

'Love III', George Herbert

Acknowledgements

In many senses this book is written for all those who suffer severe chronic intractable physical pain and their carers. It has taken longer than expected for illness intervened so I have appreciated the patience of my editor, Rachel Boulding, and her encouragement to keep going. Parts are immensely personal but I have felt it right to share these experiences openly and honestly.

However, those of us who go through such formative experience often owe thanks to many who have helped. I am no exception. A few people have been mentioned in the text but very special thanks are due to some particular friends who have stood close to us for twenty years or so, notably Janet and Stephen Baldock and Lydia Gladwin. Our friends have often proved of a sensitivity and loving faithfulness which defy description, particularly Bill and Ros Hague, Marge Hance, Bryan and Liz Wadland, Sister Carol CHN, and latterly Jenny Petersen, who as our lodger during an even more difficult time than usual, went on quietly, gently and without fuss to pray and to keep on tending the sick whenever necessary. Her calm presence continues to ease our path considerably as I write, so to Jenny and everyone else, many not named but no less appreciated, I am enormously grateful. As for the prayer, hospitality and encouragement of the sisters of the Community of St. Mary's Abbey, West Malling, my gratitude simply cannot be expressed adequately in words. Finally, Jo West and Claire Wigg put the manuscript efficiently on the word processor despite being initially startled at the contents! Thank you to them both.

On a different tack, we would like publicly to recognise

the tremendous support and prayer offered from within St. Mary's Church in Ealing, not just from members of our 'support group' there, but from many of the congregation. Now we are in Wembley, a similar acknowledgement of the care, concern and love of the people of St. John's is called for.

I must also record a debt of gratitude to so many who have shared their own hurts and pain in response to mine, but the illustrations in the text have been slightly altered and names changed to provide the protection of anonymity.

Mention is made briefly of the role of hospital pain management clinics. I would therefore like to thank Dr O'Callaghan, Director of the clinic at the Central Middlesex Hospital, for all her continuing care, effort and perseverance in working to help me relieve my pain to achieve a reasonable quality of life.

February 1992

Foreword

The celebrated nineteenth century American evangelist D.L. Moody was once asked at a meeting to introduce a notable contemporary, Henry Ward Beecher.

'Introduce Beecher?' he exclaimed. 'Not I. Ask me to black his boots and I'll do it gladly!'

I feel pretty much the same way in being asked to introduce Jenny Francis to her reading public. Having known her and her husband David for close on twenty years – beginning with a period when I was their vicar in a London suburb – I have found our roles becoming strangely reversed with the passing of time. The first time they ever came to see me they were the suppliants; they needed some advice from me about their life and their future. Jenny had just finished her degree course at Brunel University and was working in the social services department with the Borough of Harrow; David was full time in education. From time to time they would come to me for help and advice on other matters too. I was vicar and counsellor to two great and trusted members of the church.

But all that has changed. Nowadays when I get on the phone to them, and on those occasions when I visit their vicarage in Wembley, it seems that it is I who have taken on the role of suppliant and advice-seeker.

'Who is this Jenny Francis you keep quoting?' someone was asking me.

'Well', I replied, 'she's something like a *guru* to me and to a whole lot of other people when we need advice and reassurance on pastoral difficulties. It's not just that she's one of the most brilliant psychotherapists you could ever hope to meet; it's more than that. She's got a solidity and depth of wisdom that gives you confidence that – whatever the predicament she's presented with – she's not going to come up with answers off the peg.'

And where does such solidity come from? Aah . . . if we only could find the talisman! But wisdom and understanding of life do not come easily, it seems. You can be like Job of Uz, in the Old Testament – a good man, 'blameless and upright, one who feared God and turned away from evil' – and still not have a proven and rounded-off world view that understands and accommodates the baffling contradictions of our reeling planet. At least, so it was with Job, before his life was placed on the anvil of unbidden adversity. It is only towards the end of the story, when life has been stripped down to the essential person – minus the trappings and incidentals – that we find God's man has, almost imperceptibly, taken on an extra dimension, a new *authority*, that had not quite been there before. It is at the end of the forty-two chapters that we hear him saying, 'I had heard of thee by the hearing of the ear, but now my eye sees thee'.

And *authority* is what – in my eyes – characterises the author of *Belief Beyond Pain*. This is not immediately apparent when you walk into Jenny Francis' living room. Never an imposing figure from the start, now, after umpteen hospital operations, she has been sometimes described by her husband as a diminishing asset! And the pain? Where are the evidences of it? It's not on display; there's nothing to be seen, really. I do remember, coming once with a couple of friends to Jenny, inevitably for advice, and seeing her leave the room half way through the conversation. All she said was, 'Excuse me a minute; I'm just going to get a drink'. That was the only indication that her pain level had increased, and that we should not prolong our visit.

Pain and adversity. How does it fit into our view of

things? The whole point of Job's experience was that he was not – as the reader is – in the *know* as to what was happening to him. The challenge of his story was, in part, whether he could cope with the darkness as well as the light. The wind of suffering sweeps in with devastating force and the hardest blow of all is the unanswered *Why?* There are some religious traditions that will reply inexorably, 'It is the will of God'. Others will interpret suffering in this life as the just deserts carried over from a previous existence and advise the renunciation of all desire and the suppression of all true individuality. Others will serve up the superficial diagnosis that 'Satan was having a go at him'.

The immense strength within the pages of this book derives from the fact that the author has acquired over the years the credibility of a teacher and is able to look the hardest questions in the face: *Where was God when he was most needed? How does pain fit into our understanding of a loving God? Where does the Cross fit in? And, when you're in the middle of a tunnel, what on earth is happening?*

During a television interview some years ago, Malcolm Muggeridge confided, 'For me, the only great joy is understanding. This means being attuned to God, to the moral purpose of the universe, to the destiny of the human race that I belong to, to the things that are good – this is joy, and it is, of course, an experience.'

Surely that is correct. The old Anglican collect for Whit Sunday asks for only one gift – the granting of 'a right judgment in all things'. When I was younger the prayer sounded dull and pedestrian in the extreme – on this great day of power, of all days! But I have revised my estimate. There can be no greater gift or experience than that of understanding, of exercising one's judgment *and getting it right* when life seems to have become chaotic.

Belief Beyond Pain looks like filling a gap in the

publishing field that very badly needs filling. On behalf of us readers, thank you, Jenny Francis, for making the effort – in the teeth of so much that might have deterred you – to help us all . . . to understand.

Richard Bewes
All Souls Church
Langham Place, London

Introduction

'What are you writing about?' she asked.

'Pain', I replied hesitantly. A look of disbelief and perplexity followed, and the owner of the look withdrew, hastily.

Pain as a subject is still liable to make people feel ill at ease. Until very recently it remained a taboo topic of conversation in the way that bereavement had for generations. Increasingly death occurred in hospital or in other residential institutions, swept away from life in the home, unseen and mentioned only in whispers. Yet in the last twenty years or so, a tremendous resurgence of interest in understanding the grief process has stimulated the establishment of bereavement visiting schemes, research into the ways in which people cope and, on the whole, a more sympathetic attitude towards those who have lost someone they loved.

It is the growth of the hospice movement which bridges these two huge themes of life — pain and death — with its emphasis on symptom control to aid the living of life to the end. Most of us are warmly supportive of such places. We may feel relief if our dying friend or relative comes under the care of a hospice, for we trust these experts will get it right, especially where pain is concerned. It is the unimaginable horrors of uncontrolled pain that we fear most, ostensibly in our loved ones, but ultimately for ourselves. Perhaps it is this latent fear which inhibits free discussion. Faced with someone who declares they are in pain, we are embarrassed and hop from one foot to the other wondering how to respond. Thus most of us are exceedingly diffident when it comes to talking about our own pain lest we inflict similar distress or boredom on others. Many of us change the subject or hastily silence the speaker with tales of our own experiences. Few comfortably exercise compassion in drawing alongside the suffering person, unhindered by personal anxieties about future suffering, able to enter into a relationship in which the nature and effects of the pain can be shared and explored. Usually it is those who have themselves suffered who are best at this, both because they have grown into a different place in their personal journey and because their experience allows them to sense the struggles of others. That 'it takes one to know one' is quite right.

In the past few years two women have written accounts of their struggle with their physical pain, though inescapably they have shared with us the secondary agonies of what other members of their families suffer as well. Jane Grayshon, a vicar's wife in Cheshire and herself a nurse, wrote movingly of how pain feels in *Pathway Through Pain*.[1] The narrative is compelling, and for me that book was a huge comfort. Not only did Jane Grayshon herself know something of my battles, but, selfishly, I reckoned those of my friends who read and understood her position might then have a fuller appreciation of my situation too! I lent a copy to a GP friend, and she found it a helpful description of how one person fights to keep going and wrestles with her faith and trust in a loving God.

Two years ago the Christian press gave warm, sensitive reviews of *Celebration* by Dr Margaret Spufford.[2] Her life is dominated by the pain of early onset osteoporosis and her description of caring for their daughter, Bridget, born with a very rare metabolic disease, is astounding. In reading this slim volume I marvelled at how it is we can stand so much and how, in our efforts to understand, our Lord draws close.

For me, starting to write this book, it is amazing to find myself welcomed into the peace, silence and sensitive hospitality of the sisters at St Mary's Abbey, West Malling near Maidstone, Kent. Amazing, because this is where Margaret

Spufford has found her stability as an Oblate and in a surprising way my footsteps have been guided here too. And like her, the idea for this book came to me after a short article I wrote called 'Pain Hurts' was published in *Christian Arena*, the former house journal of the Universities and Colleges Christian Fellowship Association. Several people expressed their appreciation of that article and I valued their comments as some are in considerable physical pain themselves and obviously found my words had an authentic ring.

Perhaps the more unexpected response, though, was when I was asked to share the running of a workshop on coping with protracted illness at a national conference on pastoral care run jointly by several Christian counselling services. Unfortunately my co-leader was too unwell to come and the conference organisers, realising it was a possibility that this could happen to me too, had agreed to my having a back-stop. Should neither of us get to Derbyshire for this conference, then the back-stop would act as the group facilitator with the discussion topic, 'How does it feel to be let down by two chronically sick people?' as the starting point! Six other workshops ran concurrently so it was quite a shock to be told that over half those attending the conference wanted to come to mine. Feeling distinctly hesitant, especially when I saw how many doctors, psychiatrists, psychologists, clergy, social workers and other professionals were present, I asked why they had selected this workshop in particular. Most expressed their feelings of inadequacy in caring for patients, friends, colleagues or relations who are persistently unwell and in pain. Just a few bravely confessed to struggling with pain themselves. It was as a result of this workshop that this book was commissioned. I hope that it meets a need as we all become more tuned in to those in pain around us.

Pain comes in many forms, and while I too have had my

share of emotional hurt and spiritual struggle, as well as the anguish of loss, this book is an attempt to look at the physical aspect of pain. Nowadays it is becoming academically respectable to consider individuals' stories as valid. The gathering of such stories and their analysis provides material which may be of use to others. Inevitably therefore this contains part of my story, though it is not meant to be an autobiography.

My aim is to draw a picture of how it feels to be in constant pain and how it affects every aspect f life, for myself and others. In so doing I will try to explain how I cope with the apparently impossible and where I have got to in my constant efforts to do some theological reflection on it. People in general, and some Christians in particular, have views on suffering which are not helpful, so a word about friends like Job's will be included! On the other hand, all is not gloom and doom, far from it. Without the prayerful support of our friends, life would be much tougher and I hope it will become clear that the rewards of unsought vulnerability are many. I will try to share something of the public and private sides of pain, and my natural resistance to appearing weak. It seems that some, faced with intractable pain and its accompanying losses and limitations, grow bitter and resentful. Others are formed and honed till they become of impressive stature and maturity. The human spirit in the hands of God is capable of unforeseen strength and beauty, but the cost of getting there may be too high.

'What are you writing on?' asked another friend.

'Pain', I once more cautiously replied.

'Great. I'll read it if there's nothing about victorious living in it. I've had enough of that!'

1

What is pain?

'If this is mumps, it's a doddle!' I called across the garden to my husband David. We were on holiday in Somerset, and I was sitting in the sun, reading. My lop-sided face was quite amusing and we joked about the undesirability of men catching it. This was important, for this outbreak of mumps had originated with our friends' children and shortly their aunt would be marrying a young man from the same village. Better not bump into them, we said. A little more rest and the occasional paracetamol was all that was required.

Three days later I was suddenly struck by the most appalling pain in my tummy. About four inches above my waist, slightly to the left of the space between my ribs, and boring deeply, relentlessly, through to my back. I felt dreadful and lay in bed, overwhelmed, as this agony gradually spread up my back till it could go no further, having reached the tips of my shoulders. Movement was out of the question, but then that helped with the vomiting which had accompanied this unexplained development. Mercifully my distress lessened in a couple of days as the pain diminished, only to restart three days later after the other side of my face swelled. 'Doddle' was no longer in my vocabulary!

'Ah,' said my kind and wise GP once we were home, 'it must have been pancreatitis. It can be a complication of mumps in adulthood.'

This, then, was how it all began. It took years to confirm the diagnosis, for many were surprised, when, every few weeks, I was smitten by this same appalling pain and prostrated by apparently unstoppable vomiting. It lasted two to three days and very often I would be admitted to the local cottage hospital to be put on a drip and filled up with injections of anti-emetic and opiates. Sometimes the doctor used omnopon, whose very name spelt relief, conjuring up as it did a degree of temporary oblivion. Different consultants in different teaching hospitals were baffled. It looked like pancreatitis they said, but they could not prove it. I felt guilty. Perhaps it was something for which I was in some way responsible, such as the psychosomatic manifestation of stress, or the expression of other personal weaknesses.

For seven years I went to different experts. For the first five I was cared for by the same GP, who never failed to treat the problem seriously, believed in me, always listened when I moaned about how difficult life was, and striking out on his own, prescribed pancreatic enzymes which revolutionised my daily life. Increasingly offensive diarrhoea and constant nausea and vomiting unsurprisingly ravaged an already slim body, till my weight went below seven stone. Gradually, so gradually, the enzymes which supplemented my own insufficient production reduced these unmentionable symptoms and thereby reduced a little the gruelling pain which persisted between attacks.

In 1985 we moved to Cambridge for my husband to train for ordination. He was a student at Westcott House and while there we registered with a wonderful general practice. The care and concern was unsurpassed and, as each attack lengthened to four or five days, our GP visited twice a day. It was after David's ordination and our move back to London that this extraordinary disease was ultimately diagnosed at the Middlesex Hospital and subsequently confirmed by one of those complicated invasive X-rays which inject a contrast medium into the offending organ. What a relief to have a label! (Not that chronic pancreatitis is a label anyone would choose.) What a comfort to meet others in the same boat, and some who had, like me, developed it from the mumps virus. We were all the same, subject to attacks of agonising pain and, as the years went by, becoming increasingly stoical. Unlike people with other types of severe abdominal pain, we remain still and do not roll around or scream in our distress. It was this apparently odd response to pain which made our new GP suspicious of me. He did not believe the diagnosis and did not appear to believe there was a problem of pain.

How do you define pain? We all know what it is: pain is pain. Yes, it hurts. It is a discomfort sufficient to get our attention, to cause varying degrees of distress. Very useful as a warning, alerting us to danger of heat and sharp things, it can also warn us of a bodily malfunction requiring attention, or even express stress or exhaustion. For most of us, it comes in occasional acute episodes: the tension headache, the sprained ankle, or, more powerfully, childbirth or appendicitis. Severe acute pain shocks. 'Wouldn't like to go through that again', we say, the problem now being resolved.

The pain of childbirth, excruciating as it can be, is nevertheless usually creative. Its very productivity allows the mother to rise above her pain in the joy of delivery, perhaps to have subsequent babies. It is the wearing down by chronic, intractable, severe pain which proves such a challenge. Victims of arthritis respond to changing climatic conditions and form a group of people who are known to suffer. We recognise their twisted or swollen joints and go slowly to accompany their slower gait. It is the hidden pain, that which is not readily visible, which can strike and profoundly affect every aspect of life. Mine is severe all the time, though occasional days are even worse than most. I almost wish I could wear a badge so that people would know, for there is no outward sign — no limp, no cough. Only the very observant or perceptive notice a drawn face or pain-filled eyes. Paradoxically, I don't want people to know. Is it pride or embarrassment, the stiff British upper lip, or a defensive blocking off that makes me so reticent? Whatever it is and however I try to cope with it and adapt to the increasing limitations it imposes, it is a constant burden which can never be put down. When I go to work, it is with me; when we go for a walk or go on holiday, it comes too. It is my ever present companion when reading, writing, studying, in prayer, in church, in bed. It is with me now, indeed it is the prime mover in writing this book. To know that I can expect no complete relief this side of heaven is fearsome. How can I run the race which God has set before me carrying such a burden? I am over half-way to ninety and have had this for twelve years; it is a hard slog to keep going, but my down-to-earth consultant says I could live for another forty. Heaven forbid!

A sudden worsening can come any time. They say the one predictable thing about pancreatitis is its unpredictability. I can certainly vouch for that. Not to respond promptly may mean I get very cold and my blood pressure drops, but at least I've learnt how not to faint — such untidy behaviour! It upsets others too. Tiredness is the companion of pain, as many will agree, therefore it is essential to live within my limitations. This is much easier said than done, and it is not surprising that this is where the emotional ramifications come into play.

Those who have studied how people cope with grief have noticed that, by and large, the bereaved go through several stages. Numbness and shock at the outset, then denial, anger, depression, guilt in varying forms and at different times. There is no set order or time period for these but eventually, most people acquire a degree of equilibrium. Gradually, they are able to accept their loss and to contain it within themselves as their revised identity takes shape. A similar process takes place in those who fall seriously ill or are disabled by an accident. The news of having one of the most painful of all illnesses challenges its victims to come to terms with the unfaceable.

My long-suffering friends over the years will tell you about the down moments I have had and the anxiety David has had to cope with. He is the one who has to live with me, with my irritability and preoccupation, which tell him pain is getting the upper hand, with my irrational moments of enthusiasm when feeling a little better briefly. He listens to my moans and complaints, encouraging me constantly to live up to my potential and sometimes stretching me more than I wish to be stretched, so that I get cross and think he has no idea what pain is really like! This tends to happen on holiday when we tackle Dartmoor walks which are a little too long or too steep, or when we've had a particularly hectic time in the parish. Yet he is also forever helping me cut down on the commitments I take on so tfat I don't get bogged down.

Four years ago I 'retired' from my senior post with the London Diocesan Board for Social Responsibility on the grounds that I was becoming unreliable for my staff. They were social workers and community workers in the Willesden Episcopal Area of North West London (that is, the Boroughs of Harrow, Hillingdon, Ealing and Brent), sometimes working in highly pressurised settings. I felt it was not right to let people down and my use of analgesics had increased so that there were times I could not drive myself. Now I still find it difficult to opt out of my chosen voluntary activities when particularly unwell. Something inside makes me insist I should not let people down, especially when it may be a one-off talk, rather than part of a series.

People question why bad things happen, sometimes quite angrily. We are all familiar with the old chestnut, querying why God allows so much suffering, and we all find difficulty in answering, particularly if the enquirer is not a Christian. Equally, many of us are familiar with the reply made by many believers. The reply which points out how richness can come out of suffering in ways we can neither foresee nor understand, and which may imply that all will be well if we maintain our trust in our heavenly father. It is only when it happens to me, that the questioning becomes more serious and searching. I too have tried hard to understand my pain from a theological perspective, as will become clear in later chapters. My natural instinct is to be a bit of a pessimist. I'm the sort of person who will describe a bottle as half empty when it is really half full! It is accordingly natural for me to look on the dark side and see endless difficulties ahead. I caught it from my father who took the line that if he always expected the worst, any improvement on that would be a pleasant surprise! He could be a remarkably dour Scot! Even if something proved really good or even outstanding, he would say only that that was the way things should be!

Initially, my emotional response to all this pain was indeed disbelief, not that it should happen, for Christians are not exempt from suffering. It was that I was expected to carry on against such odds. Who expected me to? Possibly not one apart from me, though at times I felt driven by God. Freudians might say my superego did the driving, spurring me on to try to live life fully and attain the same high standards in all I attempted. Internal conflict was the result and one of my first victories was to recognise that I did not have to do everything at once, that it was OK to pace myself. (I am sure that on reading that last sentence David will be astonished, which will indicate to the reader that I still need practice in this area!) No longer do I think it essential to do every scrap of washing up the moment it appears! Priorities have changed radically and it is with some satisfaction that I can claim to be much more 'laid back'.

Most of us learn and grow with the passage of time. Major crises tend to sharpen our perceptions and become turning points in our lives. However, we cannot sustain the emotional stress of a crisis for long — a month or six weeks only, perhaps. Yet as we have all observed in others, major challenges and difficulties which are prolonged tend to lead towards quite a transformation. I am no exception and know that for me this process of change is inseparable from my spiritual journey. It also influences my relationships with colleagues, friends, family, church and husband, and above all, with God.

In a way, with colleagues at work, things just carry on. Some souls are more perceptive than others and I always felt it was reasonable to be relatively open about my state of health. Experience taught me that to be secretive could lead to the most fantastical interpretations — but then that's social workers and psychotherapists for you! For the last twelve years of part-time work, I have been functioning in Christian agencies. This has had advantages and disadvantages: people were supportive and prayerful, yet sometimes found difficulty in not behaving like Job's friends! I have cause, though, to be very grateful to them for putting up with all the uncertainties I brought and especially to my senior colleagues who 'took me on' in the full knowledge of my limitations. They arranged my workload as flexibly as possible so that I could operate at my own pace and in my own time.

With friends, it has been difficult. They all react differently in the light of their personalities and domestic and family circumstances. I had had a long and tedious series of operations before getting mumps so it wasn't surprising that some of our friends were becoming a little fed up with this creaky friend who seemed to need their prayers and support endlessly. Those who were further flung fared better. Oddly, those who had been closest, with whom much mutual sharing had taken place, had to withdraw. How hurtful this felt. Didn't they realise it was *their* encouragement I valued most, simply because they knew me best? Surely friends were there to assist when the going was tough?

Then through my haze of selfishness it dawned on me that for several of us the frenetic activity of middle-age had arrived. To pick up a career again and develop new professional skills, while spending time with growing children and coping with the needs of the frailer parental generation ruled out much possibility of intimate exchange! Because of my previous gynaecological misfortunes we had no children. This was probably just as well as things turned out. But our lives too had grown busier, especially as shortly before David's ordination my father had an unsatisfactory operation for a malignant tumour of the colon. His gradual deterioration and eventual death nine months later, at home, had required frequent visits to my parents' Surrey home. Necessarily, these had been time-consuming and exhausting.

Through these dark days as my pain slowly worsened, we were settling into life in a busy suburban parish where David was the rather elderly curate. In the process we made new friends who made themselves available. They listened, prayed and even offered practical help. So it was that I learnt that it could be a really good experience to find support from various sources. This way no one person became overloaded.

God clearly led us to talk to a particular couple in the church. I had felt it right to find a small 'support group' which could pray for us both and to which either of us could go to be completely open about our feelings and struggles in dealing with this worsening pain. What's more, it felt theologically right for the members of this group to be within the congregation. After a year, the first couple emigrated to Australia. This was not before one of them, a doctor, had arranged for me to see an expert in pancreatitis at the hospital in which he was doing his research. During the two long spells I had as an in-patient Bill would often quietly materialise and sit by my bed.

A new support group was formed, this time with two married couples and two single women. We had been going a relatively short time when one of the women made a very brave decision to test her vocation with the contemplative Benedictine community at St Mary's Abbey, West Malling. Had God a sense of humour? Our friend had, for as I write this in the community's comfortable Guest House, I have just met her in chapel, twinkling under her wimple, a coifèd sister steeped in prayer and monasticism, from an evangelical background! Obedience to God, though, transcends all our divisions.

So it is that, in a remarkable way, new friends appear so that the old may be retained. I hope that my friends may be less worn out now by my demands than they have been in the past! The very act of opening oneself up and being vulnerable to friends encourages reciprocity, so these friendships have from time to time proved very special. The gold brought by one or two would not have been revealed if I had not been fighting this battle and shared it with them.

Two particular situations stand out. The first, several years ago, took place when a friend only a couple of years older than I was dying of cancer. During her last twelve months we agreed to meet regularly to share and pray together. It was Sheila's own request for she said, 'I know you know better than anyone else how I feel and what the struggles are – it's comfortable talking to you, for we can cut the corners and just pick up where we really are!' And so we did. Those precious intimate exchanges live with me still. What a privilege it felt to be with a friend who chose to bare her heart and soul as she travelled the very last part of her earthly journey, visibly growing in understanding and ever closer to her heavenly father. She died smiling.

The second experience was somewhat different. A knock came at the door one day and to my surprise I found an acquaintance from church outside. She looked embarrassed and seemed very hesitant. Over a cup of coffee came the tale of her struggle bringing up a child with severe cerebral palsy. Mary's first marriage broke up because of the strain which prompted Paul's removal from home to a special boarding school a good ninety miles away. Mary's guilt was enormous. 'But I felt you would understand just because you know what it is to struggle, to be totally vulnerable, to feel a failure, not to be able to do all you want the way you hoped for.'

What an outburst. It was the first time anyone had said to me directly that my perceived vulnerability was of help to them. It required some adjustment on my part. It had not registered that my weakness, such a loss at first to me, would prove a vehicle from which others might take courage. Mary's second marriage is a huge success with all members of the family. Even Paul at a distance sensed his mother's acceptance of things and her resulting tranquillity. His progress too was marked. Gold indeed.

Very often people with difficulties only feel confident enough to talk about their anxieties when they sense it is safe to do so. If someone else first opens up revealing themselves, others follow. In some cultures not to lose face is an important social principle. Maybe it is in Britain too, though we do not recognise it in the same way.

It is often the case that families are more difficult to relate to than our chosen friends. Having no brothers or sisters and having no offspring ourselves, David and I find our friends are important to us. His family, a mother and one married sister, is small; mine, minute. We were married fairly young, at 22, in the face of considerable opposition from my parents. In a way, I suppose, it was not surprising that my mother, irrationally, blamed my earlier illness on leaving home! The fact I had been at university for four years was immaterial. What a turnabout then when, very recently, she declared she felt David had looked after me very well all these years. Of course, he had.

Clearly, therefore, it is David who bears the brunt. Sometimes he recognises signs that all is not well before I do. When things are getting bad I tend to rush around getting as much done as possible, lest for a while I cannot manage it at all. A flash of unreasonable grumpiness warns him. He alone knows how much medication I consume and inevitably he worries about the constant use of opiates. So do I, but at least they enable me to function and without them I would be tremendously restricted. There are still times when I feel terrible about what all this is doing to David. Called by God to the ordained ministry, he is saddled with a feeble, unreliable wife, who cannot do things consistently and who proves a constant anxiety and drain. Occasionally he says I'll be the death of him and, as his father died young of cardiovascular disease, I fear he might be speaking prophetically. I encourage him to eat a low fat diet which is not difficult as that is what I must stick to, but the greater the stress, the more biscuits he eats! And who can blame him?

Recently, when staying at Lee Abbey, a lay Christian community on the North Devon coast, I met someone who proved sensitive to my situation. As such people do, she enquired about the practical side of coping with this degree of pain. When I confessed that it is necessary to have several injections a day of strong analgesic, and that I never went anywhere without it, she was appalled. To be reliant on having to give oneself injections must be dreadful, and the fact that I could be suddenly smitten severely enough to pass out if I did not act sufficiently promptly, was alarming. Well, yes, I quite agree, but the human spirit is very adaptable and it is amazing what one gets used to. Even so, there are days when plunging a needle in yet again really hurts. Even with the most careful attention, nasty bruises result. What an embarrassment if the weather is warm enough to swim. The trouble is, it is not a little injection: two milles of fluid, four times a day, and of a substance which is an irritant. And with each shot is the emotional anguish of whether the pain is bad enough to warrant it, or am I merely (merely?) becoming dependent on an addictive drug. Sometimes it is possible to cut down considerably, but it doesn't last. The pancreatic liaison sister at the hospital says others have gone round that roundabout. Some, 'the successes', as she puts it, have come off analgesia altogether, but their activities tend to be severely restricted. Such knowledge adds to the pressure. Is that God's way for me? How would I cope with being a vicar's wife, let alone with everything else I do? I do not know, but for now it seems reasonable to plod on as I do, encouraged to do so by my consultant.

Nausea can be another problem, but mercifully the attacks of severe pain accompanied by unremitting vomiting seem to have stopped and no longer do I have to keep buzzing into hospital to be rehydrated.

Nausea is still unpleasant, though, and does nothing to improve one's appetite. Yet as long as it is not too bad, I have learnt to eat regardless. One must try to keep body and soul together after all. A relatively liberal use of pancreatic enzymes works wonders. Guests at dinner parties are surprised to see their hostess swallowing fistfuls of yellow and brown capsules (I can do it in fours) at the start of a meal, and are often as astonished at the end to be told that what they have just consumed was fat-free. A mistake in my choice of food usually spurs a bad bout of pain and possibly vomiting, certainly later diarrhoea. One or two other things also react, too much cucumber for instance, and coffee, especially 'proper' coffee. Most of our friends have got the hang of it now; we've all been at it a long time, after all. It is our families who do not appear to understand what 'fat' is. 'Can you have orange juice?' enquired my mother-in-law one day. 'Of course,' I replied, 'no fat in that' (said with mock gravity). 'Oh no, I suppose not', came the solemn response. And my own mother sometimes seemed to regard dietary requests as deliberate wilfulness designed to frustrate her interest in French-style cookery!

There is much discussion in the press about the validity of alternative approaches to the care and treatment of cancer victims. Some statistics show that some of those attending the 'alternative' Bristol Cancer Centre actually die earlier than control groups receiving conventional allopathic medical care. There is recognition that this may well be because their cancer was further advanced than that of the controls. Yet whenever one is called to face serious, possibly life-threatening, illness, it is beneficial to regain some control by choosing how to deal with it, and exercising a degree of personal responsibility. For this reason many pancreatic patients have turned to alternative medicine for help; I have found that an all-out attack on it is the best approach. This means that anything I can do in the way of symptom control, relaxation, breathing exercises, and general improvement in all aspects of my quality of life, are vital. Such techniques are now second nature, whether it is an attempt to be kind to myself in allowing time to get stuck into a good novel, or in switching to breath control while chairing a meeting. It goes without saying that all forms of Christian resources are part of the repertoire.

Maybe this chapter has provided a glimpse of what bearing severe pain is really like. At times there is no doubt it is absolute hell when all one can do is exist, longing for death. But there is more to it than that, for pain is very complex. In addition to imposing major physical restrictions, it also obviously involves people's emotional and spiritual lives. Mind, body and spirit are inseparable; each affects the other and it is maybe from that direction that some healing may come. Pain management clinics are relatively new but are so welcome as they encourage many to develop coping strategies beyond the pharmaceutical and physical, utilising those innate resources which rest within us all.

2

Christians' response

Having explained what happened to me, and begun to indicate some of the issues which arise for many victims of chronic pain and illness, it would seem natural for most of us to think next about our faith. How our Christian beliefs interact with life as we experience it, especially in the field of suffering is quite a poser. You will notice, however, that this chapter is called 'Christians' response', not 'The Christian response': at first sight it might appear a subtle distinction but for those on the receiving end it is significant indeed.

Apart from those who become arthritic in later years (and even then orthopaedic surgery can work wonders) and those who fall prey to other long-term or degenerative diseases, we expect most illnesses to be relatively short-term. We anticipate that our friends, colleagues and family will get better sooner rather than later. Most of us born and reared in the West in the last fifty years have a touching faith in medicine to cure at best or to relieve at least. The result is that perhaps we are less willing than previous generations to live with discomfort. Ivan Illich in his controversial writings on the growth of power exercised by the medical profession commented on this in his book, *Medical Nemesis*.[1] Our spiritual attitudes, too, reflect a similar unwillingness to accept pain. With such a broad spectrum of Christian thinking expressed these days, not just in church worship but via the media and many para-church organisations, conferences, rallies, Spring Harvest and so on, people are increasingly exposed to 'signs-and-wonders' theology. The development of healing services in parish worship and the growth of prayer cells, the burgeoning use of retreat houses and the continuing establishment of houses of healing are all part of the increased interest in self-awareness and personal wholeness. With all this going on it is hard for people to understand why disease or pain may respond neither to medical nor to 'Christian' treatment.

'God doesn't want you in pain', 'I know you won't need all those painkillers you've got, that God is going to heal you very soon.' Common enough statements, but how do they feel? After twelve years of pancreatitis I am quite an expert in hearing and receiving such well-meaning remarks. Yet always, alongside my conviction that now is not the time when God is going to heal me, comes the nagging concern that I must not be closed to that wonderful possibility. In the book *Unexpected Healing*[2] Jennifer Rees Larcombe has written recently of her astounding healing – a clear illustration of God's power at work, in his time. Some Christians are very certain, when it comes to the question of healing, of their thoughts and opinions. Others less so. Falling into the latter category, I must guard against the possibility of feeling I have failed by not being healed physically, or apparently not responding to the claims of those in the former group. Kind, sympathetic yet relatively thoughtless Christians so readily imply the 'fault' lies within the sufferer, that were he or she 'right with God' all would be well. The victim, after all, might need to confess fully or to repent of wrong attitudes, possibly inherited from previous family members and since passed to the third and fourth generations. Then there is the dreaded probe which can be so devastating: 'Maybe you're comfortable the way you are?' Of course, there are those who do not want to be better. I well remember a middle-aged housewife and mother who was admitted to the postgraduate orthopaedic hospital in which I was a social worker. She came for investigation for her back pain and paralysis. Unable to walk or even stand, she went through multiple X-rays, muscle biopsies and passive treatments, traction and rest in a plaster bed. Nothing resulted from any of this: tests were normal but function was not restored. Over the weeks we got to know each other and I discovered that her husband ran his own building business. Their three adult sons worked with him, while still living at home. Gradually it came to light that relationships between the sons were strained but, more importantly, this resulted from the apalling tensions with their martinet father whose domination was total. 'You know, I just can't stand it any more,' said this distressed woman. Suddenly all was clear. She could stand up in the family neither metaphorically nor physically, and her paralysis permitted escape. She went home in a wheelchair.

I wrote a moment ago of my conviction that now is not the time for me to be healed. What an odd thing, you may think. How can that be? Several years ago I had what some would call a spiritual experience, the like of which had never happened to me before. It has happened only once since and I will refer to it later on. On this first occasion though, I woke up one night feeling I was struggling up a rough and stony mountain track. My companion and I were wet through and trying to keep going in the teeth of a gale. 'How much longer can we manage it?' we asked each other, our heads down, battling on. It struck me that this ascent bore considerable similarity to my struggles with life in general. We talked about that for a while, how difficult and potentially limiting physical pain and fatigue can be. My companion was sympathetic but very quietly (I have wondered since how such quietness was possible in such wind) said 'Now is not the time for you to be healed. Things will go on being difficult but be reassured, I will never leave you'. A gentle hand was put on my shoulder as I turned in utter astonishment towards the Lord.

The trouble with people in my line of work is that they tend to see psychological explanations for everything. I was beginning to do likewise, so God in his wisdom took the upper hand, and I had precisely the same experience on the next two nights. There was no mistaking that! I had got the message! One of our more spiritual friends felt God does not work in such a way that he allows suffering to continue. I do not fully understand either. What I do know is that on each occasion my cheeks were wet with tears and they are again as I write – the memory is so strong and the wonder of it so amazing and powerful. And now I also know that Jesus, my companion and my Lord, has not left me, nor will he.

Jesus actually asked the man by the pool at Bethesda if he wanted to be cured (John 5:6). This is a fair question for many of us long-term sufferers, for, in order to cope at all, we have to adapt to a pattern of living which may involve opting out of certain things and relying on others for some tasks. Some perceive that there are 'secondary gains' in our disability: we maintain our sick role or remain dependent to continue receiving more attention than we might otherwise. We may wish to escape from duties we do not want to face: to be made physically well again obviously implies change. It is not unknown for amateur psychologists to assert that the chronically ill may not have the necessary will or capacity to become well. When this type of allegation came my way I was initially very hurt, then angry. Then my personal insecurities prompted a lot of self-analysis lest it be true. Yet I found no secondary gains in my life of illness and pain, only a persistent series of losses. First I had retired from full-time work, then from most of my part-time jobs and now I am cutting my voluntary activities, as pain and fatigue gain the upper hand. My husband has been forced to adapt his workload, too, but there have been, and doubtless will continue to be, many God-given opportunities for either or both of us to serve.

Given the choice, I would have preferred to bypass this route through life, yet I have to recognise the remarkable richnesses which have flowed from it all. It is this acceptance which other Christians will hail as 'healing' – inner healing. At one level they are right, but inner healing is not a once and for all experience. It is rather a state of being which fluctuates and which requires regular maintenance! There has been a veritable flood of books and articles on healing in all its aspects in recent years, particularly from evangelical and charismatic publishers. Perhaps they are responsible for those Job-like friends who point the finger with such devastating sincerity! All I can say is that of those who have found themselves protractedly ill or facing an unutterably impossible degree of permanent pain, many go through great agonies of soul as they seek to understand themselves and their suffering. Many, I know, labour to ensure that there is no block in their relationship with God, hidden or revealed, which could possibly be dealt with and removed.

Margaret was fifty when she started getting frequent headaches and feeling unusually tired. Urged by a neighbour to see her doctor, she was reassured to be told it might be the onset of her menopause. Margaret had originally trained as a nurse and felt a 'no-nonsense' approach was best, so she tried to carry on with her busy life as usual and ignore her symptoms. Within a few weeks the headache had become permanent and did not respond to her favourite pain-killer, the Anadin which she used as a sort of cure-all. This worried her and she became more anxious when she was forever dropping things. A chat with her closest friend and a careful stock-take of all her activities resulted in Margaret deciding it was time to alter her priorities. She cut out two of her major regular commitments and enjoyed a three day retreat – 'sorting myself out with my maker,' as she put it. Less harassed and hectic, she was surprised not to feel better. The day before she was due to see her GP again, hoping to discuss the desirability of hormone therapy treatment, Margaret had a fit. Admitted as an emergency to hospital, a scan indicated a sizeable brain tumour and the resulting biopsy confirmed its malignancy. Everyone was shattered. Margaret died peacefully five months later but her husband felt bitter for some time afterwards, that her determined efforts to keep going may have seriously delayed diagnosis and treatment. In a way it was understandable, for Margaret's mother had spent long years giving in to a series of minor ailments. Her daughter vowed never to be like that herself.

The other side of this coin, pinpointing lack of healing as a spiritual fault within the sufferer, is the assertion that suffering is good for you. Maybe there is a divine purpose in all this difficulty not yet made plain – patience is thus required until it is revealed; we all know that riches can be the fruit of such struggles so hold on and they will become recognisable. Of course these statements may be true but they need not necessarily be true for everyone. Whilst we believe God can cure, it does seem that there are times when he does not intervene.

Then there are those who, unable to comprehend in any other way, view affliction as punishment. When reflecting on life in an earthly family, it is easy to see how suffering may result from parental chastisement. However, our God is neither punitive nor vindictive, though he may well discipline us. Indeed, we are told repeatedly of his faithful love towards us 'since we have been justified through faith' (Romans 5.1). Therefore we can understand that 'the Lord disciplines those he loves' (Hebrews 12.6). If our distress is not a punishment, could it perhaps be sent to teach a vital lesson? Possibly – but does God really do such things? Is that not falling into the trap of vindictiveness again? Of course we are constantly learning, as our Christian belief and experience deepen over the years. Yet do we not also learn directly from his Word in the Bible, through prayer and silence, spiritual conversations with others and church worship? Those who feel they are in some way responsible for their plight, and that a lesson has to be learnt, may be trapped. They may feel that if such is God's purpose, they will be in danger of frustrating his will if they turn to 'outside' help. How dreadful to feel such alienation and how sad if there are friends around who unthinkingly subject someone to such agony.

Sometimes I wonder whether it is a sense of helplessness which spurs people to say unhelpful things to those struggling with physical affliction. A lack of patience or imagination may prompt these utterances or a reliance on the tenets of the Old Testament included in the Visitation of the Sick in Cranmer's Prayer Book. Here the capacity of God to punish or teach through pain and illness is spelt out, so maybe it is not surprising that some people still regard it as an essential part of our belief. There is a danger they may overlook the good news of the New Testament and Jesus' once and for all atonement. I will return briefly to this again in chapter four for it seems to be ingrained in many people's thinking.

Several years ago a teenager in our church was severely injured in a car crash and once his life was no longer in jeopardy, the old sages muttered that he had had it coming to him and that God was directly punishing him for his uncontrolled behaviour, and dangerous driving. Several years went by before all John's injuries were healed. During this period he made a fresh commitment to his Lord. Far from viewing his experiences as a divine punishment, he felt a deep gratitude to God for coming close in his distress. His recommitment and his obviously vibrant relationship with Jesus the risen Lord served only to reinforce the sages' original claim that this was God's way of 'bringing him to heel'.

How is it that otherwise dear Christian friends can make over-confident statements about our weaknesses and chastise us for our spiritual frailty when they would not dream of such dogmatic utterances in other contexts? For some, at least, it is the only way of relating when mystified at God's purposes and feeling helpless in the face of such pain. Those who have been bereaved through the death of their partner testify to similar attitudes as friends and neighbours cross the road to avoid the embarrassment of conversation. They no longer 'fit' socially either, as so much of our social life revolves around couples; many husbands and wives no longer invite a newly single person. Their presence makes others uncomfortable and may be an unwelcome reminder of their mortality. Similarly, the presence of people in pain proves powerfully that there are situations in which neither medicine nor prayer solve the problem. To stand out in this way can be too threatening for many, so frequently the subject is swept under the carpet. It may turn out to be those with whom we have relatively little contact who are most helpful as they themselves are not threatened and are more able to absorb the facts and consequences of our limitations.

All of us have been nurtured in our Christian life to believe that we are never tested beyond our limits. Often we quote relevant chapter and verse to our desperate friends ('A bruised reed he will not break', Matthew 12.20), confident in the assurance it offers. But we also know that there are times when suffering may be too much to bear and people do crack, crushed by their tremendous burden. How do we explain that? Sometimes, when reflecting on pain and anguish, there are no ready answers. Those who are sensitive to the pain of the world are aware of the paradoxes. As I write, much of sub-Saharan Africa is facing yet another catastrophic famine and US politicians are deciding when to launch a ground offensive against Iraq which will cause huge casualties.

It is my experience that in persevering, it is astonishing how elastic our inner resources prove to be. From somewhere deep inside, and from deep within my relationship with God, comes an ability to cope with things I would never have thought possible. Through this process I am stripped utterly of all but the essentials, and thereby begin to glimpse what the writer to the Hebrews meant when he wrote in chapter 12, verse 11 that hardship later on 'produces a harvest of righteousness and peace for those who have been trained by it'. Yet I have moments when I do not feel sufficiently heroic for all this and I have lost two friends whose load proved too heavy, one through suicide and one who died as a result of anorexia nervosa.

* * *

Many pain-bearers comment on the clear feeling we have that because we are not outwardly healed we are in some way beyond the pale – I call it 'the leper syndrome'. The syndrome combines the feeling of failure, in its broadest context, with the sense of being 'different', almost untouchable.

Several years ago, I tried to explain this 'leper' feeling to a close friend. She was quite unable to grasp what I was trying to convey, saying, for example, 'But what do you mean? It's not as if you have a skin disease, or even cancer, which I suppose people are afraid of in that way!' I just could not get across the way in which many cannot cope with protracted illness in others. Unsure how to respond, what to say or even unsure about the possibility of touch, lots of people shy away. It is less embarrassing that way.

However, there is something very significant, one might go as far as to say powerful, in the touch of another. Once, when overwhelmed totally by the pain and when struggling hard not to faint, a pair of hands gently moved to and fro across my back. They even got the right spot, not bad for a non-medic, and thereby I felt the sensitive concern of someone reaching out to me in my distress. They were the hands of love and unconditional acceptance.

As I write, a particularly sad situation comes to mind. A man in his forties had terminal cancer and though there was not much time left, his wife could not bring herself to show him any physical affection. Her fear was that she might somehow 'catch it' and either fall ill herself or pass it on to their children, whom she forbade, incidentally, to visit their father in hospital. The wife's agonies of soul were bad enough, realising as she did, there was no factual evidence of contagion to support her belief. Her husband's isolation and hurt governed his last days, but his gracious understanding of his wife's dilemma and the dignity with which he coped, were profoundly moving. Even in his almost unbearable pain, he sought to accommodate his wife's needs.

So far, in this chapter, it would appear that most of the Christians I have encountered would appear to be distinguished by their arrogance and assertiveness, or their insensitivity and lack of insight. Of course, things are not as gloomy as this. We have some close friends with whom both my husband and I can be completely open about our struggles. Several of them formed the little prayer support group I described in the previous chapter, interceding on my behalf when pain is getting the upper hand, and thanking and praising God for his goodness and love. These dear souls are a wonderful God-given resource for us and they responded so sensitively when asked to form such a group. People often rise to the challenge if we are clear in describing our needs. To offer someone a role or task puts boundaries round an otherwise bottomless pit of suffering and they will fulfil all that is required. It is a good lesson to learn. People function better if faced with a measurable task and that holds true for supporters and sufferer alike. We too then, are not overwhelmed by the enormity of our distress.

Many years ago, when training as a social worker, I remember being caught up in a lengthy discussion about whether it was possible to identify with suffering if one had not suffered oneself. I cannot remember what we concluded, though there was a strong feeling that what counted was having enough imagination to put oneself into others' shoes and so be truly empathic. There are occasions now when, I must confess, I would like others not merely to know how severe my pain is, but how it feels. I wish they knew that the effort to keep going feels just like the exhaustion experienced by a mountain-climber, when continuing to put one foot in front of the other seems an impossibility. Once, when I was still in a hospital bed after having had a hysterectomy the day after my twenty-eighth birthday, a friend who was eight months pregnant visited me. She spoke in an embarrassingly strident voice about her pregnancy, and almost accusingly about the way in which God healed those with one hundred per cent faith and trust. Sadly, a few years later the same friend wept copiously after the same operation, not for the profound loss she had sustained but because she now knew at first hand what it felt like. 'I had no idea what you were going through, no idea at all.' My tears flowed as well, for I could hardly bear the thought of her having to face whrt had cost me so dear.

It is much easier to criticise than to draw alongside and stand with a person in pain. However, a slowly growing number of people are preparing themselves or are already prepared to do just this. The growth of the hospice movement has inspired many to appreciate the challenges of coping with protracted and severe chronic, rather than terminal, pain. Bearing in mind St Paul's teaching about the different gifts we all have within the body of Christ, this is a welcome development. Others have acquired much wisdom from the changes and chances of life in general, and those with the maturity and sensitivity to stay with those in pain are worth their weight in gold. At such times many would-be helpers gladly respond to specific requests which are easier to deal with than open-ended ones. Involvement like this permits people to grow more confident in helping others without exposing them to anything too harrowing or demanding.

No doubt we all vary in our need of help as well as in the kind of help which is appropriate. For us, prayer support is vital. So also, for me particularly, are certain sorts of practical help. I can do the housework, but the exhaustion that results is disproportionate to the task in hand so I am most appreciative of the help our Margaret brings every Wednesday. That frees me to do other, less physical, things. People often seize upon the request for practical assistance with alacrity so occasionally it is quite difficult to satisfy a genuine offer of help if there is nothing obvious waiting to be done. I know of others who struggle with the gardening or the shopping but are quite unable to respond to the person who says 'Don't hesitate to let me know if I can help in any way.' The open-endedness works both ways. It is so much easier if the well-meaning friend makes a tangible offer, such as, 'Can I cut the grass for you regularly through the summer?'

I commented earlier that when I started writing this book last summer it was with some surprise I found myself at Malling Abbey. That is where I am again, greatly comforted by the warm welcome and the perceptive care the sisters offer. The accepting nature of this contemplative community and other religious as they practise hospitality, gives tacit permission for people in all sorts of conditions to seek their aid, both physical and spiritual. This is in contrast to the strain of very definite and relatively rigid Christian teaching about personal responsibility. The boom in interest in retreats, Ignatian spirituality and opportunities to be still and apart from the world, speaks of our natural appreciation of non-judgemental acceptance. The swing by some evangelicals away from the relatively noisy and dogmatic aspects of their style of worship is less of a surprise when the unconditional love of Christ is demonstrated so powerfully in a place of quietness such as this. The capacity to live with issues and challenges as yet unresolved is a sign of maturity, and is nurtured more in some kinds of spiritual traditions than in others. In the last ten years, many practising counsellors and psychotherapists have had direct experience of helping those the Church has failed. Sadly this has frequently been because no one listens accurately and/or because newcomers (and others) may be labelled in a judgemental way. Jesus' gentle acceptance of those who came to him for healing is a wonderful model of how we should relate to others, meeting their physical needs first. By careful listening through our own stillness, we meet God in many of those we seek to help. What a privilege that is!

3

My response: Responsibility

In the first chapter I painted a landscape picture of how I cope with pain and included glimpses of how others are affected. Sometimes I think it would be good to be as thick as two short planks so that I did not feel compelled to reflect on it at all. I fondly imagine blind acceptance might be easier. But my way is to try to understand, to harness my brain to work through all aspects of my illness, for it is only that way that I am able to do my best in all departments of life, as a human being interacting with others, as a wife, a colleague, a patient, but above all and in all and through all, as a Christian.

In evangelical circles it is not uncommon to hear the phrase, 'so and so has a high doctrine of responsibility'. At first I did not know what this meant; then I realised that admiration was focussed on those who had high standards in all that they did. This included living an exemplary Christian life, publicly espousing moral values which might well make them stand out in non-Christian circles. I was impressed and found myself consciously trying to do the same. Perhaps this was not surprising; I have already admitted to being a natural pessimist, now it is time to confess to being rather a perfectionist as well. Coupled with a relatively strict Calvinistic upbringing incorporating elements of stoicism and fortitude, it is little wonder that protracted illness, particularly pain, forced me into rigorous self-analysis. How easy it was for me to be hard on myself. Physically, I drove myself, and emotionally I agonised about whether I was in some way responsible for my own pain. After all, although Christians are not exempt from illness and suffering, maybe I was not 'right with God', for it did seem that the pancreatitis had followed a long succession of operations which, at last, had dealt with all my other medical problems. My medical friends groaned at 'yet another' thing. Well, I thought, I must not give in, but rather work at this.

Fortunately, the passage of time and increasing physical limitation, combined with God's gracious help, have worked wonders so that I have been freed from the shackles of the negativity of that part of my inheritance! I do still feel that I must always do my best, but my best need not be 110%! It seems right to do as well as I can in all my activities, given the circumstances at the time; that is what my best is. I am reminded of this when at Malling Abbey. Some regard the Benedictine Rule as pretty tough, but St Benedict himself stipulated that religious should be expected to do things only 'as they are able'. Such gentleness is the key to many things and has opened new doors to me, giving me permission to cease striving and to try to understand only that which is understandable. When trying to help those with emotional difficulties, I am very good at encouraging them to rest or to be kind to themselves, to take the pressure off and learn to 'be'. Only the other day, when I had to cancel an appointment with a very experienced psychiatric social worker who comes for supervision, she sent a card saying, 'You are good at telling others to rest, make sure you do too!'

This response, to do my best in all things as I am able and to seek such insight as is possible, is fairly obvious, perhaps. We all respond to challenges in our unique way and even perceive different challenges in similar situations. For me the issue of trust became important: trust in my heavenly father and thus through God, trust in others and myself.

The next chapter on healing, wholeness and growth will develop this further, but here it is appropriate to introduce the central notion of trust.

Recently Jane Grayshon was the subject of a television programme called 'Encounter' on ITV, in which she asked the question, 'Is it wise to trust in a loving God?' With a history of thirty operations in fourteen years and a daily quota of nagging pain, many would understand her asking the question. Readers of Jane's books and poetry will be familiar with her feelings and the way in which she feels the Lord has enabled her to cope. She has a significant speaking ministry and thereby a valuable mission to many. Knowing her history, a lot of people, especially non-Christians, would think it foolhardy to trust in God as she does. My own mother, soon after my father's death, asked, 'How can you go on believing after all that's happened? What has God ever done for you?' Three years on she has difficulty even framing that question as in her hurt she feels there is no God. To ask the question presupposes his existence.

And what has God ever done for me? What has he not! As I write, I have just paused to read Psalm 125: 'Those who trust in the Lord are like Mount Zion, which cannot be shaken but endures for ever.' The wonderful graciousness of God in drawing close over all these years, working greatly in me to change my attitudes and to help me come to terms with my lot, has been remarkable. From a fearful, timid person, lacking confidence and self-esteem, I now know that nothing in heaven or on earth can ever separate me from his love and that, against all the odds I can honestly 'be joyful in hope, patient [usually] in affliction and faithful in prayer' (Romans 12.12).

Jane said she feels disappointed in God whenever another crisis occurs; other people feel angry. Both reactions are understandable. Christian people not uncommonly make the mistake of believing that in any eventuality they will respond in a Christian way. Yet in a crisis we react first as people, humans, with feelings, previous experiences, hopes and fears. That, after all, is why Jesus entered our human state. It may only be after the initial impact that we recall our specific Christian resources and turn to God. Just before he retired, Archbishop Robert Runcie was commenting on the start of the Gulf War and pointed out that it is often not until the going gets tough that most people pray. He understood their motivation and unlike some others who were critical on the grounds that people cannot be bothered with God when all is well, he felt that the instinct to turn to God in danger is sound.

At present it is fashionable to identify the key elements of our personalities so that with heightened insight we may understand ourselves more fully and so live and work more effectively. Many have done this using Myers Briggs personality tests and there are now available analyses of how different types pray better when relating to God in a spiritual mode with which they feel comfortable. All this eagerness to understand ourselves is fine as long as it remains a tool to help us grow in our spiritual lives and does not become either an end in itself or provide us with excuses for getting out of things we should be facing. For me, to be able to understand and integrate the attitudes inherited from my family with the main strengths and weaknesses of somebody with my temperament has proved very useful, especially as it eventually sank in that God does accept me as I am, complete with thorn in the flesh. There is therefore no reason why I should not accept myself, indeed, there is every reason why I should!

The freedom that this has provided has correspondingly paved the way for more openness in all relationships. No longer do I feel overwhelming reticence in sharing with others, having instead the confidence to explain myself appropriately. I have already mentioned how the recognition and acceptance of my own vulnerability seems to have signalled to others that it is safe for them to own up to their own needs. What a sad comment it is on our Christian lives if we cannot admit our weaknesses or discuss our challenges with our friends and neighbours for fear of being regarded as letting the side down. Sometimes it seems that our non-Christian friends are more accepting than our fellow heirs in Christ. Whereas the latter group may have a tendency to judge us by our spiritual fruits, and physical health for them is one such, the others may simply raise the ancient query, 'If you believe, why isn't God making you better?'

Jesus said that whoever loses his life for his sake, will (paradoxically) find new life in him. When working hard in his service we often do experience a kind of loss of our life, and wonder at our capacity to forget ourselves as we concentrate on others. The trouble with those of us who have to struggle with physical affliction is that it forces us to dwell on ourselves. It is pretty well impossible to rise above such pain for long as it bores its way through my body, demanding to be noticed. And yet, and again paradoxically, relating to friends and acquaintances becomes more honest and hence richer. I think this has to do with priorities.

When life is stripped to its bare essentials and it is not possible to do everything one would like to do, priorities have to be reassessed. Because my energy is limited, I am motivated to conserve as much as possible, thus communicating more directly and leaving aside non-essentials. In other words, by and large, I am learning to 'cut the cackle'! The spin-off of this is being able to get to the point more readily, though there is a danger of becoming too abrupt.

When meeting new people, conversation tends to focus around 'getting to know you' questions such as whether you have children, are married, work and so on. It is as if by the attachment of labels we find something to grasp and relate to, rather like a handle. It is difficult to know how to respond if there are no such handles and most of us, even if unconsciously, seek labels as a way of being rooted in society and being afforded certain status.

When I was a child, my mother would occasionally meet a 'girlfriend', as she called them, who was either still single or if married, not yet a mother. It is not clear in my memory whether my feeling that those women were not relaxed in the presence of children was really my perception or some vague attitude transmitted from my mother. Somehow they seemed stiff. I used to be quite afraid of little children at one time, too. After all, how is one supposed to relate when childless oneself and an only child? Gradually, all this has regained its proper perspective but many find life very difficult if they are unable, or do not have the opportunity, to fulfil their hopes and aspirations. With approximately ten per cent of couples being infertile, we read regularly now of their deep distress and frantic attempts to conceive or adopt. In Britain these days there are exceedingly few babies available for adoption so pressure is being exerted on the government to legislate for inter-country adoption. Few set procedures yet exist so would-be adoptive parents go to great lengths and considerable expense to acquire a child and slip it through immigration controls. This and the growing role of surrogate mothers, as well as complex and expensive infertility treatment, highlight the desperation of women (and some men) in this position. It is not simply the biological creative urge but also the perceived stigma of involuntary childlessness with which people wrestle. Single women hoping to have a child as virgins is the latest twist in the tale.

Over the years I have developed a technique in response to queries about children. I simply say that I was not able to have any but that we do enjoy our thirteen God-children and we can give them back whenever they are awful! Such a reply lightens the mood and deals head on with the question so many dare not ask: which partner was to blame! By taking the initiative, fantasies no longer surround my long-suffering husband! It is unfortunate, though, that a person is often unconsciously blamed for their inability to conceive. Blame reminds me of Old Testament mores which should have been abandoned by 1992!

Of course, I have a role as Vicar's wife, but because illness has forced me to stop most of my paid professional work, and as we have no children, I really have no labels. When I retired (for the first time) in 1979, it was with considerable dread that I approached all this looming space, lest I had to measure 'out my life with coffee spoons' (T S Eliot, 'The Love Song of J Alfred Prufrock').[1] However, God knew otherwise as he helped me to find new interests and to develop the old ones further. Because I had such an inheritance of feeling worthless, I thought I badly needed labels to survive. Yet God in his mercy sorted it all out and now I practically never register all these losses, confident in my identity as one of his children. That is all I need. How I reached such a position will be covered in the next chapter but as people do not know how to relate at first to someone who does not fit into a role or category with which they are familiar, it is important for me to take the initiative and explain my situation, thereby scotching any fears and fantasies they may have.

When planning this slim volume, my husband, David, offered to write a chapter from his point of view. Then we giggled and asked each other if that would break up our marriage! He is the only one to live through my pain with me and overall he is the most thoughtful and sensitively helpful friend. I feel very sorry for him. Having married all those years ago (in 1968), he too has seen loss succeed loss. The impact of childlessness hit him three to four years after I had worked through it and then he had to cope through three years of my repeated gut obstructions with three more operations and the huge haul back to relative normality, only for me to catch mumps and be repeatedly devastated by these acute attacks of pancreatitis. My weight loss was such that by the early 80s he often told friends that I was a diminishing asset! When I look at him, perhaps from a distance across a room, the lines of concern etched in his face and the greyness of his beard, turning to white, fill me with such love and compassion I would do anything to spare him further anxiety. Sometimes I'm tempted to keep from him just how I am feeling, but he says he has to know, for that is the only way he can cope. We have both learnt, eventually, to face pain head on. There are other times, though, when I wish he could know what it feels like so that he would not expect me to do things I am not up to – that is when my selfish side comes to the fore; not very edifying.

'You don't want to let anyone know you're a bit down – they soon get fed up with it,' said a middle-aged friend whose entire life to date has revolved around loss. 'It's OK to recognise it and to struggle with it on my own,' she continues, 'but I couldn't possibly expect my colleagues at work to have to keep on making allowances.' She was speaking from the pain – emotional pain – of her circumstances but it was a familiar theme. It is all very well to work hard at all the things which are my responsibility and to try hard to maintain normal relationships with friends and colleagues. Naturally this involves appropriate mutual acceptance, give and take. It is quite another to be working closely with others whose loads may increase if I cannot deliver the goods or who may be accountable to me as their manager. There is quite a tension between struggling on at work because it does not seem quite right to 'give up' (such a pejorative phrase!) and the huge effort it can be to continue providing the professional support structures on which less senior staff depend.

In recent years, as I explained earlier, I made a point of being completely open with employers and have tried to ensure that colleagues know what is what, too. Nowadays being free from vomiting and hence the need to be whisked into hospital for rehydration means things are more stable. Coping with constant severe pain nevertheless takes its toll and perceptive colleagues begin to learn to read the signs. It is important for them, and for personal clients, to know that broken appointments are not a rejection of them, it is simply that my pancreas is misbehaving.

When I was a little girl my mother took me up to Glasgow for two weeks every Easter to see my grandparents. Travelling nearly five hundred miles by train was quite an adventure. I liked staying in their bungalow and having outings on foot or by tramcar with my grandfather. Life there had a strict routine for immediately after lunch my grandmother disappeared into her room for her afternoon rest. I understood this was because she had 'a bad heart'. Enjoyment of our stay was tempered by this because Grandma was prone to turning a nasty shade of grey and appeared not to be able to speak till someone found her 'pellets' (as she called them) and things were restored to normal. She always walked very slowly and avoided hills and steps. My anxiety was directed towards some imagined emergency and I spent quite a lot of energy searching Grandma's face or interpreting her body language in an attempt to forestall any potential disaster. This was how I learnt to interpret non-verbal clues at an early age!

Knowing that friends and colleagues are pretty good at this too it seemed right for me to protect them. I therefore retired again. Although it is good to be surrounded by such kind and attentive people, there are moments when I get fed up and would like to be the same as everyone else. Alternatively there are times when I am struggling, maybe even fairly desperately, and nobody else notices. This is not necessarily when I wish others could experience it for themselves! Rather, this is a time of greatest challenge to me, to put into practice my belief that others – husband, friends, colleagues – must be allowed sufficient space to forget about it. It is not necessary for them to share my burden all the time, but for me the discipline required to step back into my pain in order to free them is one of the greatest challenges. Not to permit withdrawal, which is, after all, a safety measure, could be to drive someone to breaking point or to drive them away in self-defence. Thus there is no escape for me and I am the one who must facilitate the temporary withdrawal of my nearest and dearest.

At work, ordinary professional structures provide some protection for everybody, but even there colleagues had to be prepared to step into the breach. Whenever I accept an invitation, whether it is to deliver a talk, run a study day or baby-sit, I always must explain it is possible I will prove unreliable and a back-up would be a good idea. After all this time people are beginning to get the idea! It still irks me to have to do this, but that is reality, and the acceptance of my potential unreliability is another part of my load.

Relationships with the medical profession are a significant part of life when persistently ill. The relief when a firm diagnosis was eventually made was tremendous but in time that became tempered by my new GP who though he never said so, clearly did not believe it. With the proposals for a much-reformed NHS under scrutiny, he took the line that my pancreatic enzymes would be too expensive to prescribe, that I could no longer attend the Middlesex Hospital as he would be contracted to send his patients somewhere nearer and cheaper, and that my reliance on pain relief was addiction.

The support given by the Middlesex has been superb and mercifully, my husband moved to be Vicar of Wembley which remains within that hospital's catchment area. Eventually we settled down with a kind and sympathetic single-handed practitioner nearby and at our request she referred me to a local pain clinic. Once again, the relief at being heard accurately by someone who knew what he was dealing with, when talking about my pain, was wonderful. This consultant anaesthetist accepts the use of opiates in the relief of chronic severe pain and sanctioned their continued use. I am so grateful. He feels only those with dependant personalities become addicted and so I felt vindicated in my efforts to retain the use of my effective pain-killing injections. The result is that I can contribute both to the life of our parish and to a restricted range of professional activities. It seems just a little arrogant/unfortunate that my surgeon, who disapproves of continuous analgesia (for reasons initially not explained) should thereby limit severely the quality of life of his patients. To be as restricted as some of them are, when means of relief are at hand, is hard to comprehend. For myself, I have made the choice to live life as fully as possible – after all, Jesus came that we should have life more abundantly! If this means availing myself of controlled drugs, so be it. This way I can at least be more creative and less demanding, to say nothing of being better tempered and easier to live with. Yet to sanction their use in no way obviates the need to continue developing other coping strategies as well. Some fear that continued use of medication or any other clinical procedures serves to reinforce the model of being 'sick', but after all this time I am convinced that by using such devices efficiently and effectively, life is made more normal rather than less. Just the other day though, it was pointed out to me that Jesus, in agony on the cross, did not accept the proffered sponge (Matthew 27.48). Should I therefore, they asked, abandon analgesia?

Relationships with doctors and other health service professionals are so important. With the exception of one GP we have been very well served by doctors, whose own ethos has often been Christian. I believe that what is required is a good doctor first and foremost, so it has been a bonus to find we share Christian values, and the sense of security experienced is considerable. It is in the surgery that the private struggles with illness and pain link up with the public persona and it is probably only our long-suffering doctor, close friends and my husband who know the intimate details of the struggle on a day-to-day basis. Because appearing in public looking ghastly causes others to be anxious, I tend to appear only when looking at least reasonable. I regard this as sensitivity to others; is it also pride? I am not sure, but I would like to think not. In a way, always to put others at ease is an extension of social skills training.

The business of covering-up is an odd one. Apart from distressing others (and memories of Grandma are still fresh), obvious illness or pain can detract from the matter in hand, and may well cause the sufferer embarrassment and anger when Christian friends respond critically. Guilt, too, can arise in the patient when illness persists and the doctor tacitly seems to blame him for his failure to improve. In the same way that some doctors were said to hasten past the dying patient when doing a ward round before the hospice movement got going, embarrassed by their impotence, so today many find it exceedingly difficult to stay alongside those with severe but chronic problems. Patients like to please their doctors, being almost childlike in hoping for praise as they make progress. To get beyond all this and to put responsibility back where it belongs can be quite tough, particularly on the patient and his family. Fortunately more care is taken now over the vocational training of GP's but patients can still be subject to bad doctors' arrogance and power.

A barrister friend has commented how often he has noticed that people's illness, disability or the progress of their disease do not fit exactly with their doctors' prognoses. They often seem to come away feeling guilty, almost as if it were their fault for letting the side down. He said, 'We must remember the medical profession is there to help us, we don't need to be apologetic if our symptoms are not what they think they should be. It is just that doctors have all the power, which makes us feel more vulnerable if we cannot be categorised, or if we remain chronically unwell!'

So it is that my own experience and my observation of others led me to conclude that it is essential for those of us who suffer protractedly to be self-aware and to be adept at utilising our personal strengths. But this can be done effectively only when submitted totally to God. For most Christians, different chapters of their lives reflect a greater or lesser degree of submission and obedience in their walk with their Lord. As I said earlier, to yield completely and to remain content is a continuing process which requires working at! Yet through it all somehow comes the extraordinary and, for some, quite unexpected capacity to cope. We have been given individual strengths of character, family or friends, all within the framework of God's surpassing love. With his help, it is up to us to be as responsible as we can over the use of these precious resources, even although there are, and will be, moments when we would prefer not to know, and we wish, like Hezekiah, to turn our faces to the wall! As a parting shot, I believe a sense of humour to be a vital part of the equipment too.

4

Towards healing, wholeness and growth

'Ah – the crunch chapter!' A friend had noticed the chapter heading when I had left my papers lying around. 'Well, it is, isn't it?' he defended himself. 'After all, that's what we're all aiming for, to be open to God's healing power and to claim our wholeness in Christ Jesus.' Another friend who had dropped in melted discreetly from the room. We both knew it isn't that simple.

In recent years there has been a rapid growth of interest in personality types and the development of certain classifications as analytical tools. As I have mentioned, the Myers-Briggs Type Indicator is one in popular use and there are other systems which have their loyal adherents too. These include transactional analysis (TA) as well as several methods more formally based on Freudian, Kleinian, Jungian and other analytic insights. Their usefulness lies in offering a route towards self-knowledge and a greater degree of insight into how people tick. Some Christians find this is all very suspect, but many are happy to make use of an appropriate framework once it has been tried and tested against Christian doctrine.

Through these forms of personality analysis, people seem to find it easier to accept one another's differences, indeed, to value their varying qualities. We discover that we all cope with things differently. I found it useful to ponder on my coping mechanisms, hung as they are on to a fairly introverted, intuitive personality. The techniques we employ to defend ourselves from the slings and arrows of the world were often learnt unconsciously at home before we were independent. In adulthood, professional training may modify them, as well as the influence of our personal value systems and psychological make-up. Nevertheless a significant factor in the way we react to any given situation rests within personality type.

Often, when working as a hospital social worker, I would get to know a patient who would eventually confide that the one thing they dreaded had now happened to them, almost as though it were a self-fulfilling prophecy. Bill was just such a person. An enthusiastic young man who liked to live dangerously, he always rushed everywhere and used up a lot of energy so that his slim figure appeared taut with suppressed tension. It seemed he never relaxed. His manner of driving reflected this lifestyle until one July day, on holiday, he was involved in a very serious road accident, and was literally brought to a halt. In hospital for most of the next three years, facing a series of operations to rebuild his shattered legs and pelvis, Bill confessed his blind fear of having a crash, and recognised that this anxiety affected his driving. He saw his recklessness as 'an accident waiting to happen', and now that the very worst had occurred he felt set free. Psychoanalysts have a contribution to make here in helping us understand how such things occur, possibly even encouraged by our individual character and temperament.

The one common childhood illness to which I seemed immune was mumps. There were at least two epidemics of it during my secondary education and the children of friends had had it since. Oddly, it was the one disease I felt wary of but it passed me by and I did not have to cope with the facial disfigurement and discomfort which everyone said was horrid. Until . . .

Thus for me to catch mumps of all things and then to try to deal with it in my normal introspective way led me back into the trap of pessimism. For periods of time in the decade before catching mumps pain had proved a major problem for me, first with ovarian cysts and then gut obstructions. Eight operations, while nothing like as many as Jane Grayshon has undergone nevertheless took some getting over. The long haul back to normality can be tedious and requires emotional strength in addition to physical healing. Yet it was soon evident that that last surgical intervention in May 1980 had worked well and David and I heaved sighs of relief as we began to look forward and plan for the future, something we had been quite unable to do when stumbling from one hospital admission to the next. The freedom from pain was wonderful.

It was against this background of joy and relief that the after-effects of mumps emerged. Within a few months it had become clear that acute attacks every few weeks were to be the norm, an utterly appalling prospect. To be so ill for twenty-four to forty-eight hours every three or five weeks was extremely disruptive and, though the severe pain diminished with the cessation of vomiting, some pain did persist from one episode to the next. It was at this point that David felt let down and angry, and, because I myself could barely face the situation and its implications, stunned into disbelief at this new twist of events, I could not help him either. Gradually, very gradually, my instinctive urge to question reasserted itself in a bid to reach at least some kind of comprehension and thereby relative emotional equilibrium. To achieve some degree of emotional stability, however, did not itself bring healing. Instead it heralded the beginning of the process which is still going on, the acceptance of all this pain with God's grace, to the point at which I can say with St Paul that I am content in whatsoever state I find myself. This is the story I will now try to outline.

It has become evident that my efforts to understand what was happening to my body were frequently being freshly challenged. When someone is suddenly acutely ill, for example with appendicitis, their friends and family allow them to assume the role of sick person. Then, as they recover, so they are encouraged to pick up the threads of responsibility again. Something different happens if the incapacity is chronic and long-term. Obviously not all diseases are painful, but the limitations imposed by chronic illness can be severe enough to disrupt well-established patterns of daily living. In such circumstances the need to adapt is paramount if the victim is to go on contributing to life and gaining something from it. To my shame I must confess that I used to regard those who remained unwell as rather wimpish, or trapped into negative behaviour by as yet unresolved emotional difficulties. Talk about judgemental!

Stephen Pattison, writing in *Alive and Kicking*,[1] points out that the role of the ill is to wait and see, in faith, whether they get better, as they are usually seen as 'impotent' in effecting their own cure. For the chronically ill and for those in continuing unremitting pain, I think it is different. Most of us feel some sense of responsibility towards 'getting ourselves better', using whatever tools are at our disposal, and often aided and abetted by those around us. As Stephen Pattison says, 'the vast majority of contemporary Christians respond to illness and healing in ways which are probably outwardly indistinguishable from those of their non-Christian neighbours. That is to say that most Christians see illness and healing primarily in organic terms and seek cures from modern medical methods' (*Alive and Kicking*, p49). Despite the current revival of interest in religious healing, most people probably still view it as a last resort, lumped in with other forms of alternative medicine.

One of my inheritances from childhood was an over-developed sense of guilt. It surfaced noticeably after the mumps but before the diagnosis. Surely it must be my fault that all this pain kept overwhelming me when eminent doctors could not name the illness. Had I lacked faith when I was anointed and others prayed (as described in James 5)? Was I being very slow in the uptake when God was trying to teach me something important? Perhaps I was being tested to see how my loyalty stood up to adversity, or perhaps I was clinging on to unconfessed sin and was not, therefore, 'right with God'. Indeed, was God himself the author of all this agony, or was it that he allowed it to happen without actively intervening to stop it? I rapidly rejected the idea of God as the initiator of suffering but for years anguished thoughts about the other possibilities would creep unbidden into my heart and sometimes they would be fuelled by the well-intentioned remarks of friends or colleagues. Perhaps most Christrans are vulnerable to the ideas of the 'lack of faith' school, if only because we know what weak creatures we really are. I felt very sensitive to it, and still do, concerned as I am not to let my Lord down. I know that God works for the good of those who love him, but it still felt too much to accept. Some of our friends tried to reassure me that God must have some hidden purpose in it, not yet revealed, which would make it all worthwhile. That seemed pretty tough too, and until today, all these suggestions about the cause of protracted suffering seemed non-starters, for God, despite appearances, is, I believe, a loving God who is not vindictive. But today, while leafing through the Order for the Visitation of the Sick in the *Book of Common Prayer*, I stumbled upon the following sentences:

> Wherefore, whatsoever your sickness is, know you certainly, that it is God's visitation. And for what cause soever this sickness is sent unto you; whether it be to try your patience, for the example of others, and that your

> faith may be found in the day of the Lord laudable, glorious and honourable, to the increase of glory and endless felicity; or else it be sent unto you to correct and amend in you whatsoever doth offend the eyes of your heavenly Father; know you certainly, that if you truly repent you of your sins, and bear your sickness patiently, trusting in God's mercy for his dear Son Jesus Christ's sake and render unto him humble thanks for his fatherly visitation, submitting yourself wholly unto his will, it shall turn to your profit, and help you forward in the right way that leadeth unto everlasting life.[2]

A note follows that if the person is very sick, the next bit may be omitted. It begins 'Take therefore in good part the chastisement of the Lord: For . . . whom the Lord loveth he chasteneth, and scourgeth every son he receiveth.' So it continues. While it is clear that as a child of God we may be subject to his discipline, as we were to our earthly parents, it is much harder to appreciate the other sentences.

It is not surprising that this office, or its modern-day equivalent, is omitted from the *Alternative Service Book*, published in 1980.[3] Perhaps it reflected seventeenth century thinking about affliction, based as it was on Old Testament teaching without reference to Jesus' healing power or the other promises expressed in the New Testament, such as that in James 5.13–17.

I have met the occasional Christian who believed that as long as they kept on the right side of God all would be well and they would 'earn' protection from any significant suffering. As far as I am concerned Christians cannot be exempt from pain and illness and there are countless published accounts of people's experiences in illness, handicap, accident, death, bereavement and so on. They commonly also describe the process of adjustment which their heavenly father, in his mercy, sees them through. Even so, they are not all reports of victory. Some are heart-rending, and happy endings are not guaranteed.

In acknowledging God's sovereignty and electing to travel along the road of his choice, I have yielded myself to him completely. There are rare moments when feeling a little better temporarily, I bounce a bit like Tigger, and fall into the trap of doing things in my own strength. One might reasonably suppose that by this time I might have learned to resist such temptation, for I trip myself up every time! How easy it is to write those words, 'I have yielded myself to him completely'. What a struggle it is in reality. It is a hard and bitter agony to die to self and live to God when it means following God's path for us. On bad days I feel totally unequal to the task of running the race that is set before me. A deep weariness pervades the hidden reaches of my soul and in my fatigue and weakness I can do nothing other than depend totally on God. That is literally all I can do, all I can be. But wait, it is in accepting my weakness, so that I am wrapped in the Lord's love, that I become strong, immensely strong, girded by his power and love. I know now that nothing, nothing at all can separate me from him. We have all heard these things before and we may cluck approvingly when someone testifies to such an experience, without reflecting just how difficult it is to reach that point. It takes great courage to allow oneself to remain in such weakness, to be exposed, stripped naked in all senses before God himself. Bereft of clothes, layer upon layer of self stripped away to reveal a puny body and a more puny spirit, we find our feet placed on rock and know in our innermost being that this is God; he it is who wraps us in his love but does not necessarily exempt us from the world's evil.

For many, and perhaps for evangelicals especially, it sounds excellent to have learnt such lessons and to be able to claim the victory of Christ crucified for ourselves. But it is not quite like that. Whereas Jesus died once, for all, I know I have to keep working at it. It is not a one off experience, rather a process through which we often struggle, aware that in it God will draw as close as we will permit.

* * *

Years ago, when doing my social work training, my tutor let slip the comment, 'growing hurts'. It certainly does! Many find their crises in life eventually lead to a point of emotional growth which others recognise from their developed maturity. A friend in her thirties has recently had major surgery, having rarely been ill before. At one level she enjoyed all the attention lavished on her by her church friends. Realising all her family are in Australia, people consciously stepped into the role of substitute relatives. At quite another level, though, both the experience itself and her reflections on it afterwards have proved remarkable growing points as she gained a fresh understanding of the meaning of vulnerability. Yet she commented that while appreciative of such insights, she would not choose to gain them by going through surgery like that!

Many experience illness, possibly pain in particular, as a formative experience. Had I known what was coming, I would have turned tail and fled. Fortunately we do not know what our future holds. For I would have missed out on God's wonderful revelation of his love and the opportunities I have had to know so much more of him. From the utter poverty of my pain and debility have flowed riches beyond compare. I could do nothing else; weakness in all departments (body, mind and spirit) compelled me to depend on him totally, and from such trust, by his grace and mercy, have come such treasures. I am deeply aware of the fact that this treasure is in 'jars of clay' (2 Corinthians 4.7). My jars feel bashed and chipped, but even so they are the vessels which show God's all-surpassing power. 'We always carry around in our body the death of Jesus, so that the life of Jesus may also be revealed in our body. For we who are alive are always being given over to death for Jesus' sake, so that his life may be revealed in our mortal body.' (2 Corinthians 4.10–11.) No wonder there are times when I find it impossible to offer myself at the end of the communion service in the words, from Romans 12.1, 'Through him we offer you our souls and bodies to be a living sacrifice'. It is more than I can bear. But I can now, in my weakness, not flee but rest in our Lord Jesus Christ, thereby keeping open the way for him to use my battered self as he wishes. The dichotomy of offering everything yet realising it is so little, of experiencing such joy in his presence, the fruit of death, yet knowing tears are close, led through suffering, perseverance and character to hope. 'And hope does not disappoint us, because God has poured out his love into our hearts by the Holy Spirit, whom he has given us.' (Romans 5.5.)

C S Lewis, writing about the function of pain in our lives, described it as God's megaphone. When our lives are so full and we are rushing from one thing to the next, we can be remarkably deaf to him! He therefore shouts at us through affliction. This approach recalls the words of the Visitation of the Sick in the Prayer Book: it seems there is no escape from these teachings. I have met many people who testify to learning much through their difficulties. For them it would ring bells. We often think God arranges things so that an opportunity for growth is created. Does such an approach tally, however, with the teaching that our Lord is a God of infinite love, who is not at all vindictive?

'Have you ever prayed for healing?' asked a new friend recently, who was then treated to an explanation of how long I have been ill and how prayer for healing is not an intermittent cry from the heart when things get too much for David and me. Instead it is a regular feature of our prayer life and we can both recognise God's intervention in many ways throughout the last eleven years. 'Surely you have not just accepted it, though?' came the horrified reply. 'Umm, well . . . yes, in a sense, and remember Paul's thorn in the flesh?' 'But God does not want you to be like that,' was her response.

I often wonder how well-meaning Christians can be so certain about it. Can they even begin to imagine how I prostrate myself at the foot of the cross as I learn to live the tension between unresolved pain and the knowledge that he can heal, and does, in his own time? How can they be sure God does not want me like this when I am reassured through my listening to God that now is not the time? Surely God is not in conflict over this. So, very hesitantly, I begin to say something about my experience. But my friend cannot hear.

In the increasingly understood field of bereavement, the ultimate goal is seen by many as the absorption of their loss into their whole persona so that it is part of them, contained within their life experience. So the grieving person may come to terms with their loss and find a new identity. Some describe it as acceptance.

Acceptance is a term occasionally thrown to us by the medical profession: 'You'll have to learn to live with it', 'You'll just have to accept it – come to terms with it', I have heard my consultant surgeon say to other pancreatic patients. Some people misconstrue the word as meaning giving in, not trying any more, an opting out of conflict. It is not like that at all. To experience something akin to the bereaved as they work towards a new identity is to know what an enormous struggle it can be, quite the antithesis of opting out. For those apparently being called to live a life of severe pain, it seems an impossible prospect. Can you imagine what it would be like for you to be told the pain you now know will increase with time and as yet there is little to be done about it? In several different contexts I have learnt that when difficulties arise it always pays to face the situation head on honestly, realistically and with a minimum of delay. To accomplish that when burdened by a painful load would seem to be asking the sufferer to face the unfaceable. True acceptance is a monumental step; it is hardly a light decision made on the spur of the moment. It often takes years and some never achieve it. They may remain too angry or resentful or, sadly, unable any longer to trust in a loving God who appears to remain aloof and does not draw alongside to rescue them in their distress. It signals the culmination of the struggle to adapt to this appalling load, the point at which our Lord meets us and comes with us in our efforts to grow through all the emotional and spiritual challenges en route.

Brian and I met whenever he came to the artificial limb and appliance centre where I worked. Regular visits were required for a while as he had recently had his stump trimmed and the old artificial leg, which had been his companion since soon after the war ended in 1945, no longer fitted properly. But this was not his main problem and he shrugged it off as an understandable result of warfare. The contrast between this acceptance and his rage and bitterness at having lost his sight in an industrial accident in the early 60's was shocking. He had been unable to work since and had almost totally failed to adapt to his blindness. Periods of acute depression alternated with bouts of enormous hostility and anger and while many friends and former colleagues were sympathetic, Brian could not receive from them at all. Gradually their number dwindled so that by the mid-70's he had become an embittered and isolated elderly man.

In almost total contrast, Geoffrey coped astonishingly with his old war wounds. He lost both legs at the battle of

Alamein in the North African desert and was forever being admitted to hospital for the extraction of splinters of shrapnel which kept 'rising to the surface' as he put it. As part of both buttocks had been blown away, artificial limbs were not an option but he became independent in his wheelchair and used his lively mind and administrative skills in a variety of ways. I met him when asked to provide him with home tuition for one of the Open University courses he was doing. He finished his honours degree two years later. It was Geoffrey's wife who privately admitted to feeling her life had been shattered. Yet she felt it imperative to care for him as lovingly and faithfully as possible in response to his bravery and determination not to become an invalid.

Some of our Christian friends recognise the fruits of my battle, for now I need struggle no more; I can relax, assured of God's unfailing love and acceptance of me. While the pain remains, boring through my body, remarkably I feel at rest, a sense of peace pervades my soul, while my friends tell me that I have experienced 'inner healing'. What a victory, they chorus! *I* know, however, fresh challenges will arise. This is no 'victory'. I am not in control of it. It is simply that in my weakness I can do no other than depend on God and his grace is sufficient, and will be sufficient.

One of the lessons we all must learn is to leave our unnecessary baggage of life at the foot of the cross. It has been borne in upon me afresh recently that not only did Jesus die for me, he understands and can carry *all* my burdens. Elsewhere I have mentioned the need for those of us who are chronically ill to work at coping with it and to work at relating to friends, family and colleagues around us so that they, in turn, are comfortable with us. Similarly we need to recognise and deal with the unresolved elements of our lives which may cause concealed emotional or spiritual pain, adding to the load we already carry. To dump these at the foot of the cross frees us in a way nothing else can. As we travel on through life so we must repeat the process, like regular spring-cleaning. We leave behind those hurts and struggles which only Jesus can take away. It is the dark side of our natures which requires such attention even if the darkness did not necessarily originate with us. I wrote about the negative character of my own self-denying stoical inheritance; for some, such negativity may have been passed down through the generations not in any deliberate fashion, but simply as part of a system of values and outlook absorbed unconsciously.

So it is that healing comes in various guises and life's experiences facilitate personal growth, as, tempered by God's love, they become a source of blessing and help. Appropriate acceptance of our lot, and the love of God through our Lord Jesus Christ guide us towards a wholeness which cannot be complete this side of the kingdom.

5

Reflections

Many who have experienced severe illness or injury say afterwards that they noticed a marked increase in their sensitivity to beauty in the world around them, seeing with fresh eyes the loveliness of a rose or the majesty of the mountains. Affliction can, for some, still the heart in such a way that the contrast with the dark side of life and struggle is very clear, and strength is gained from a range of sources such as music, poetry and art. For some, though, the contrast seems so stark that God feels utterly remote; while most of us take the delights of creation for granted and pass by relatively oblivious. It was with some surprise that simultaneously with this increased appreciation of the world around, I realised I had an affinity with those in distress, in some way I do not fully understand, within the core of my being I could sense pain in others. Readily moved by other people's troubles or achievements, or stirred by some beauty in the field of the arts I find myself often moved to tears. To have the opportunity to relate to people going through such a period is a privilege, though in our haste we often overlook Paul's injunction to the Romans to 'weep with those who weep' (Romans 12.15). It seems that this heightened sensitivity is a by-product of acceptance, for, in reaching a point equilibrium, there comes freedom from concentrating so much on self, despite the paradox that one of the troubles with pain in particular, is the insistence with which it demands attention to self.

Acceptance is something of an adventure for it is not at

all clear where it is going to lead! It is not a once and for all thing, either, as I indicated in the last chapter, though the point bears repetition. In the same way that we commit our lives to Christ and have to keep doing so afresh during our lifetime, so acceptance of my particular thorn requires a willingness to yield and be open to changes which might not otherwise happen. I find it difficult to explain how this process is any different from a life given up to God's will: those better versed in the spiritual life might be able to put it into words. It is somehow on a different and deeper plane, for although as Christians we look for God's leading and do our best to hear and obey, the extra dimension of pain in some way adds to that.

Some of my friends view my life as a series of losses: first not being able to have children, then being compelled by illness to move from full-time to part-time work to work on a consultative level for a few hours a month.

It is not all loss, however. For simultaneously other doors are opening, ones which I would not have thought of knocking on, almost as if God takes away with one hand and gives back with the other. The request to write this book, was a surprise and already more writing requests have been made. It seems that God is gently steering me, at a pace with which I can cope, from the more active to the less active. The influence of the life of the Community at Malling Abbey is profound and while there to write, one cannot but be aware of the presence of God and be alert to his promptings. So I have come to recognise the value of the contemplative life and feel myself increasingly drawn to it. When sensing the power of this place, it makes me think that living the contemplative life would not be such a bad aim for a Vicar's wife! One of the sisters commented that quite a lot of people are aware in middle age of such a personal development. It is reassuring to know I am normal in terms of human growth and development!

It is nevertheless important not to deny personal losses, for only by recognising their gravity and grieving appropriately is it possible to come to terms with them. Then they can be integrated properly and become part of me. In accepting the way things change and being prepared to have a go at the fresh challenges which arise is stimulating, and being unforeseen, quite exciting.

Out of all this comes great richness, maybe of a kind and quality I would not have thought of twenty years ago, but rich and very precious all the same. Through this background of pain I feel I have been given such a lot. Yet I cannot help being mindful of the fact that to whom much is given, much is required.

I have never found it necessary to wonder 'Why me?', though it eventually dawned on me that I did not need to add to my pain by self-inflicted anger, guilt, frustration or other negative feelings. I remember, years ago, feeling quite angry when friends, close friends in particular, clearly did not appreciate my struggle to come to terms with childlessness. How could they? They were busy procreating and trying to keep their heads above water with the daily round of playschool, washing, keeping up their professional lives. Thus they had neither time nor space to perceive the battles of their one childless friend. In due season I came to terms with that and with God's help, let it all go.

When pancreatitis struck years later, there was no need to repeat some of those negative experiences. But, my goodness, the physical pain was extreme, far worse than ovarian cysts twisting or gut obstructions. Mercifully the acute attacks then did not last long. It is more recently, in the last year or so, that the pain remains severe all the time, and at odd moments I do get cross when I feel forced to do more than I am able. No longer, though, do I get frustrated, at least, not very often. In the same way, I seem to be free of the self-imposed loneliness which descended in heavy clouds when I had struggled to come to terms with being so very different from my fertile peers. Self-recrimination is not helpful. There have been occasions in the past when that has been a temptation but over the years I have found peace with my maker and am now confident it is not something I have done, or failed to do, which has caused all this suffering. To reach such a position is such a relief and leaves me free to get on with coping as best as I can. It requires a constant watch, though – smugness and complacency are not temptations. It is all a struggle.

There is one aspect in particular that I am not so good at. It is being completely honest with David. I try very hard not to hide things, but sometimes he feels I am being devious when I am temporarily reticent in an attempt to give him a patch of relief and space. One of the most difficult aspects of severe chronic illness is, I find, the pain and distress it causes those who are closest, in my case, my husband. I find that particularly tough and yet there is nothing I can do about it, except commit it to our heavenly father and keep working on it.

What is extraordinary in all this is, as is perhaps becoming apparent, the discovery of resources far beyond those you thought you possessed. In her book *Celebration*,[1] Margaret Spufford says the same thing. When they felt utterly stretched, they found their elastic limit was further on. Somehow in the nightmare of suffering we seem to be given strength to keep going. Margaret hints at the relief given by continuing her academic work despite her own physical limitations and even when being with her sick daughter in busy teaching hospitals.

So how did we discover the 'loaves and fishes' principle applied to our resources? Last winter we learnt more of these things when my mother slipped in the bath and cracked a couple of ribs. Unable to breathe deeply enough because of the pain and being a smoker, she rapidly developed a severe chest infection. Suddenly my struggles went onto the back burner as I travelled round west London to her Surrey home several times in quick succession over a ten-day period. Refusing to go into hospital or to come and stay with us or, indeed, to take up her neighbours' offers of help, she was dependent on me. I think, rather sadly, that my mother felt somewhat neglected, but as I saw things, it was amazing that I had just enough energy to do what was necessary. God's economy saw to it.

Feats of human endurance like Margaret Spufford's are moving and some of us, naturally, find them inspiring, not least in the wondrous way God makes us so aware of his abiding love. As the years have passed by, I have found increasingly that my obvious vulnerability seems to have helped others while their experiences have, in turn, taught me much. They indicated clearly that from somewhere in it all, could come good.

When people meet great personal difficulties or tragedy, some find their very foundations shaken and in their distress wonder where God is. Sadly, for some, this leads to a lengthy estrangement or even complete severance from their belief. Others 'go the other way', as they say, and find comfort in religion. Perhaps there are times in our life's journey when we feel alienated from God and can only cling on to what we know intellectually, and it is as much as we can do to exercise a discipline of faith. This can be so painful yet somewhere in the recesses of mind and heart we know we are not forgotten. Time and again God reveals his faithfulness to us – it is we who shake! Then again, there are other times we are acutely aware of God's love being poured out on us, not despite but through, our sufferings. As Henri Nouwen has written, in a passage drawn to my attention by one of the Malling Sisters:

God is a compassionate God, a God who comes to share our lives in solidarity. He has committed himself to live in solidarity with us, to share our joys and pains, to defend and protect us and to suffer all of life with us. How do we know this is anything more than a beautiful idea? We know this because in Jesus God's compassion became visible to us; he was the concrete embodiment of the divine compassion in our world. When the Gospels speak of Jesus being moved with compassion, they are expressing something very deep and mysterious, related to the most vulnerable part of his being. When Jesus was moved to compassion, the source of all life trembled, the ground of all love burst open, and the abyss of God's immense, inexhaustible, own unfathomable tenderness revealed itself. Jesus the sinless Son of God, chose in total freedom to suffer fully our pains and thus to let us discover the true nature of our passions. He lives our broken humanity not as a curse but as a blessing . . . God's compassion is not something abstract or indefinite, but a concrete, specific gesture in which God reached out to us. To us who cry from the depth of our brokenness for a hand that can touch us, a word that speaks to us here and now and a heart that is not afraid of our fears and tremblings; to us who feel our pain as no other human being feels it, to us a man has come who could truly say 'I am with you'.[2]

Recently a friend was telling me about the physical and emotional agony she experienced at the age of eight, when she was persistently sexually abused by the family's male babysitter. For decades she put it into the back of her mind until the burden of it became too great and it surfaced in untold distress. Where was God when he was most needed? Why had he not protected her and where was he now in the reawakened nightmare? 'I didn't think I had any more to say to God', she said. Then one day, she was filled with the realisation that Jesus had been with her all the time. He too had been abused, he too felt the agony, he too had carried this load with her for all these years and now he was still loving her, faithfully sharing her pain. She has been such a help to others who have had similar experiences, able to help them make the psychological shift from seeing themselves as dirty, worthless victims to believing their true value in God's eyes as precious survivors. The following poem by Muriel gives a glimpse of her anguish as she journeyed on to the point of being able to write this beautiful poem.

Within the stillness – love

Be still my soul
and know your God
within

I long to love and trust you,
but find it hard to see
how you, or any other,
could possibly love me.
Or how see me as lovely?
That's quite another thing!
Tears of pain and grief
flow from deep within.

Be still my soul
and know God's love
within

I bring to you my pain and tears,
my heartache and my grief.
Tossed about by doubts and fears,
my times of unbelief.

So many issues unresolved,
but this is what I bring.
Can you accept and love me
just as I am
within?

Be still my soul
and hear God's voice
within

In the stillness of my night
you whispered in my ear:
'You are precious in my sight
and I love you. Do not fear.
I have called you by your name,
you are mine.
Be not afraid.
I am here
within.'

Be still my soul
and worship God
within

As Mary bathed your feet with tears,
loved you and adored,
So through my tears I bring to you
my gift of love outpoured.
You hold me close, my soul is stilled,
I know your words are true.
And in your ear I whisper back
'God, I love you too'.[3]

We see God's living presence in others around us and those recovering from a time of testing, an operation or acute illness, redundancy or bereavement frequently testify to his grace. I know I would not survive intact without his ceaseless care and because of this outpouring of his love and changeless energy it is a privilege to try to reflect it to others, or maybe simply to let it pass through me in whatever way I can. This could be in church circles or seeing people professionally through a time of emotional need. The context does not matter – we never know when we might be entertaining angels unawares. The Benedictine reception of guests as Christ is a good model to emulate.

In opening up to people in this way, it is perhaps not surprising that some remarkable, precious and hitherto unlikely friendships have developed. It is as if my heavenly father has taken me by the hand and introduced me to some very special people. The first of these meetings arose when David and I attended a retreat at Lee Abbey in Devon. The brief ten minute conversation with the Retreat Leader, Sister Carol, of the Community of the Holy Name, has led to a continuing and deepening friendship. David is part of this process, just as he is involved with the developing link with St Mary's Abbey, West Malling.

Since the publication of Joyce Huggett's influential book *Listening to God*[4] and its sequels, the evangelical world has become much more sensitive to, and appreciative of, the silence and discipline of monasticism. It is only, as I write, a year since I went to stay at the Abbey for the first time and it is a link I treasure with the utmost gratitude. God surely does work in an amazing way and has an obvious sense of humour. Whoever would have seen my life being full of nuns, so to speak! Their interest and concern, however, tells of yet another truth, that it is only those who can accept my pain as an integral component of the person that is the me I now am, who fully appreciate the situation. I am not the person I was ten or twenty years ago but am instead an imperfect, suffering servant of Christ whose treasure is to be found in surprising quarters on earth but supremely in God the father. Our friends who can accept me without wanting to change me and who understand the redemptive work of God, are a great blessing. There is always, even in the darkest reaches of my night, a slender golden thread somewhere which makes it bearable.

In responding to others, having received so much myself, it is always my favourite text in Galatians 6 which comes to mind:

> Carry each other's burdens, and in this way you will fulfil the law of Christ. Let us not become weary in doing good, for at the proper time we will reap a harvest if we do not give up. Therefore, as we have opportunity, let us do good to all people, especially to those who belong to the family of believers (Galatians 6. 2, 9, 10).

Similarly, I see it as my responsibility to work on my own pain, in the same way as we are encouraged to work at our relationships within and outside marriage. By this I mean I must take the initiative to seek to understand both how pain and illness affect me as a person, as a child of God and in relationships with others. To be able to explain something of it to those about me seems to put people at ease. My acceptance of the status quo and the knowledge that it may well get worse, as it has done already, are important in how I handle pain and its increasing limitations. Side by side with that acceptance, which can be quite frightening if I give my imagination full rein, is the need for me to accept difficult relationships with friends or family who cannot cope with it. It is for me to allow them to question or express their anger or frustration, or indeed, even to withdraw.

Despite all the kindness and treasures which I have received, and continue to receive, I still need all the help I can get. Margaret Spufford's book, and Jane Grayshon's too,[5] have been of particular value. It is largely, though, the reciprocity within the body of Christ which contributes so much. This, in a way, has been borne in upon me through writing this book to a degree which I had not fully appreciated before. The unconditional love of God and the love, encouragement, practical and spiritual support of friends, our support group and the community of Malling Abbey as well as Sister Carol, are all unmeasurable. In particular, the enthusiasm shown by the sisters of Malling and their efforts to welcome and care for me whenever I have been able to stay for a few days, have spoken to me of this reciprocity. It is less easy for us to give back directly to a community whose life is largely hidden, other than by union through prayer. Yet if this slim volume can be of help to others, and if in the course of my life on earth, I may continue to reflect such bounteous love as I have received myself, I could not hope for anything more eloquent.

Conclusion

'How can you write a conclusion when it's all still happening?' queried a friend, reasonably. Insofar as we continue to grow and change on our pathway through life, there may be no point at which it is particularly appropriate to draw conclusions. Some elements of discovery do, however, stay with us, even if subject to adaptation as we continue to be moulded by experience. One of these discoveries is the realisation that my life is a reminder and sign to others that a major component of our faith is based on the cross. There are times when that facet is overlooked, its essential nature too uncomfortable to accept. As one of the Malling sisters put it,

> White light is made up of colours of the spectrum. There would not be that transparent purity if there were no dark indigo included. And the rainbow that shows each shade is the sign of God's covenant.

For the last few months, the pain has been getting worse and I have had greater difficulty in controlling it. The resultant tiredness has meant I have coped less well and in my moments of despondency found myself wondering whether I had anything at all of value to say in this little book – surely others managed their pain and illness so much better? Credibility, I thought, would be stretched as I struggled to avoid an emotional boggy patch. Doubtless it would be better if I just shut up! Then a new factor was introduced to the equation. What about trying a type of nerve block? The understanding consultant of the pain clinic had registered my distress, and was offering to perform a minor operation in the hope of reducing the pain level significantly. God seems to have heard our prayers and his answer is that once again, I shall be admitted to hospital. And what if it does not work? Then it may be that there will be a rethink about a more suitable regime of medication and other strategies.

Despite the worsening pain, one week in particular stands out from last summer. It was spent at Lee Abbey. Our friends, members of the Community, joined with me as we listened to God together, seeking fresh insight into my pain and seeking to know God's will and purpose. It was one of those times which live on in the memory, partly because of the kindness and sensitivity of our friends, but largely also for the way God worked. An amazing dream came for three consecutive nights. I shared it with our friends, and for some, the meaning was a straightforward reassurance that Jesus can bear all our pains and burdens if I only let him. However, on further reflection, I felt uncomfortable with that interpretation and gradually found myself drawn to a much deeper understanding of Jesus' acceptance of our flawed humanity and the wonderful way he not only shares our afflictions but also enables some people to draw specially close and to share something of his own agony on the cross. Others have commented in recent years that they felt I was being asked to share something of the crucifixion with him. At first I rejected that observation, sure that such a profound spiritual experience happened to others, not me, and that anyway there was no way in which I could possibly be worthy of such an awesome privilege. God seemed to be reinforcing it, however, in such a way that there could be no doubt. Most of us would shy away from any physical experience of crucifixion if offered a choice. I feel the same. Yet God, my heavenly father, is gently pointing out that as a child of his, a member of the body of Christ, my suffering and struggles are one with his. I am almost overwhelmed by his graciousness in giving me such a powerful experience.

In the midst of life is death. We are constantly reminded of this as the seasons succeed each other. Seeds are sown, flourish, fruit and die, and in their death are the seeds of future recreation. It is the same with us. Aspects of ourselves die as we grow through life, giving way to a richer maturity, a wisdom born of the integration of life experience and a contentment to leave unresolved those questions and experiences which we cannot yet understand. So it is that I am no longer subject to strong feelings of inadequacy because I am not physically healed, or, worse, feelings of inferiority because in some sense, my faith and trust in God is seen by others as wanting. Christians are not exempt from suffering and though, for me, the question is not 'Why?', but rather, 'Why not?', I have reached the recognition, with St Paul, that God's grace is undoubtedly sufficient. So I can accept the mystery of my pain, warmed and encouraged by the astounding privilege of sharing Christ's sufferings and even more aware of God's amazing love for his children.

It was in reaching this point, with the realisation that my experiences and efforts to deal with the 'changes and chances of this fleeting world' are unique and valid, so that I felt able once more to hold my head up. Though the physical pain persists, the attitudes of others are no longer part of the affliction! Paradoxically, it is when so low, for whatever reason, that *all* one can do is rest utterly on the Lord, that one then becomes strong. So it has been for me, and it is in that state that from time to time God may provide a flash of insight. Also, in being constantly aware of his care and love, the very penetrating sense of isolation is relieved. Again, paradoxically, it is this very strength that enables me to stand humbly and vulnerably at the foot of the cross, shocked afresh at the magnitude of it all. Jesus has gone through all this, for me.

It is a funny thing, but well recognised, that many of us enter the so-called caring professions out of an unmet need in ourselves. This need may be deep in the unconscious, not even acknowledged yet. It may, of course, be a direct result of a good experience on the receiving end. It is not uncommon, for example, for people to go on to some form of counselling training, having been first restored themselves. A friend and former client did exactly that and is now nearing the end of her course, already establishing her reputation as a competent, perceptive counsellor. Books and articles on 'the wounded healer' abound and I am not alone in experiencing the remarkable way in which people come to share their concerns, sensing in us the vulnerability which they may also be feeling. That recognition seems to remove any perceived potential threat. We all respond differently to our particular pain and some people are able to transcend their sufferings in quite a heroic or noble fashion, others are not. There is nothing heroic or victorious about my struggles. Indeed, as I have admitted, there are times when death would slip in as a welcome friend; 'To live is Christ and to die is gain' (Philippians 1.21). But what a privilege it is to share others' suffering; no words are adequate to describe the opportunity to share Christ's sufferings in my body. There are times when it becomes so hard that I cannot help but pray it may pass me by. But 'My grace is sufficient' is the phrase which echoes and returns, and I know to be true: 'Yet not my will, but yours be done' (Luke 22.42). I can face this journey only in the sure knowledge that I will be accompanied.

Challenge and response

Our life
moves in two worlds
time
and eternity
and both are
glory

here
glory in pains
sweet gains
there
glory
alone remains[1]

An Afterword by David Francis

> No man is an Iland, intire of it selfe; every man is a peece of the Continent, a part of the maine; if a Clod bee washed away by the Sea, Europe is the lesse, as well as if a Promontorie were, as well as if a Mannor of thy friends or of thine owne were; any mans death diminishes me, because I am involved in Mankinde; And therefore never send to know for whom the bell tolls; it tolls for thee.[1]

It now seems to me that I was extremely foolhardy to volunteer, at the planning stage, to offer to make a contribution to this book. But there it was, in black and white in the final draft which Jenny asked me to read, the record of my offer to write a chapter from my point of view. The problems inherent in this were many . . . Where should I begin? With the events of the last eleven years, when Jenny has suffered increasingly from the pain associated with chronic pancreatitis? Or should I return a further ten years to that unlooked-for and, at the time, quite mystifying earlier apprenticeship on the receiving end of things medical? Then we were confronted first by the complications of diagnosis and, for her, the pain of Jenny's gynaecological condition, secondly by our resulting childlessness and thirdly by a series of operations attempting to rectify the problems which arose as a result of gynaecological intervention. Where should I end? . . . With a chronic condition, particularly one which inflicts severe and unremitting pain on the sufferer, we have found that it is unwise to assume that a plateau can be achieved: the illness and the body can both fluctuate as the severity of the pain increases or the toleration of the pain-killing drugs grow or their absorption decreases.

Should my contribution be a commentary on what Jenny has already written, with all the problems that that might imply of repeating much of what she has described or of producing what might seem to be a critique? Or should it be a separately conceived consideration of the implications, for a spouse, of living with a partner suffering from chronic, non-terminal, pain?

A commentary seemed to me to be inappropriate, and the more I thought about the latter option the more, it seemed to me, it could become a book in itself. I have therefore limited myself to a few reflections which seem important to me now as I seek always to understand more fully the implications for her of the pain which afflicts Jenny every minute of every day, and thus support her as best as I can.

'. . . one flesh . . .'

One of the joys of the parochial ministry is the opportunity to meet those who are preparing for marriage and to explore with them something of their expectations. Inevitably this reminds me of our own marriage nearly twenty-five years ago. In the marriage service in the Church of England's *Alternative Service Book* – which came after our wedding, although much of the phraseology used is similar to that in use then – marriage is described as 'a holy mystery in which man and woman become one flesh'.[2] Recently, commenting on this with couples preparing for marriage and speaking about it in my address during marriage services, I have drawn attention to how true this can be. As the couple grow together, the husband will increasingly know how the wife will react in particular situations, the wife will almost unfailingly know what the husband will say or do before the words are uttered or the move made, and vice versa!

In spite of this, however, it is still possible to have secrets from one's spouse; deliberately to withhold all or part of the truth, often with the best of motives. It may be done in order to give a pleasant surprise, as with a birthday or Christmas present, or it may be done in order to shield the partner from something that could be hurtful or depressing. There may be no problem with this in certain circumstances, but if it becomes a normal practice it is like the malfunctioning of the nervous system in the human body. That system is designed to transmit sensation, including pain, and if the transmissions do not get through the body can be endangered. If a hand is placed on the hot-plate of a cooker, unaware that it is on and the nervous system is not picking-up the messages from the surface of the hand and transmitting them to the brain, far more damage will be done to the tissues than the slight burn which would result from the instant withdrawal that would occur when the temperature of the hot-plate was sensed. The equivalent situation is true in the context of the 'one flesh': if the communication system within the marriage does not work, then injury may occur. Both parties need to work at this – in our situation this means that I must be really open to receive full information on Jenny's current condition and she must be willing to share that information. When one is all too ready to block-off and the other to withhold the true situation there is danger.

In contemporary comment, on matters of national security or commercial secrecy, the 'need-to-know' formula is one that is used to describe a limiting process in which information is only revealed to individuals in a situation on a strict and narrow interpretation of actions they need to take on the basis of that information. While this may be one way of running the secret service or a business (and in the latter context it has recently been subject to criticism in the media following revelations of practices within the commercial empire of the late Robert Maxwell) it is certainly no way to run a marriage!

In the context of the 'one flesh' there should be no restrictive filter of this sort between the component parts. With certain exceptions, we have tried to keep the lines of communication open, but those exceptions, however understandable in themselves, have required careful appraisal. If I fail to hear or observe what I should be aware of, or if Jenny obscures the situation in order to avoid worrying me, assumptions can be made which are ill-founded and can be harmful. In the one situation she may assume that I am aware of the real situation when I am not, in the other I may believe I have the measure of it when I do not. As a result we may tackle something which, in the event, proves to be over-demanding: Jenny will then become exhausted and less able to cope with her pain. Furthermore, because of the way in which this has happened, the misunderstanding that occurred because of the malfunctioning of its 'nervous system', there is damage to the 'one flesh' which needs patching-up.

'. . . in sickness and in health'

The promises in the marriage service draw attention to potential changes of situation that may occur as each takes the other as their spouse:

> . . . from this day forward;
> for better, for worse,
> for richer, for poorer,
> in sickness and in health,
> to love and to cherish,
> till death us do part[3]

Not surprisingly, in the period of preparation for marriage and at the service itself it is generally the 'better', 'richer' and 'in health' elements of these contrasting pairs which are predominant in the minds of the couple, and in the thoughts of their relatives and friends. The preface to the service is, however, appropriately cautionary: it says marriage

> . . . is a way of life that all should honour;
> and it must not be undertaken carelessly, lightly, or selfishly, but reverently, responsibly, and after serious thought.[4]

It is to this sentence that I habitually direct the attention of the prospective bride and groom when we meet in my study. I do not wish to be a prophet of gloom, but I do feel it important to explore with them the extent of their 'serious thought', how 'responsibly' they have considered together their potential reactions to times that are less good. Everything may not always be as it seems to them now, in prospect; there will be low times as well as high times – 'for better, for worse'.

Inevitably every couple assures me that they have given 'serious thought' to this. Indeed the initial planning of the wedding itself may have introduced unexpected tensions into a previously unstressed relationship as decisions need to be taken – how many guests? what degree of formality? what sort of reception? whether to 'obey' or not?! – the possible causes of stress at this stage are numerous! Very few couples are really able – like one young couple we know where the prospective bride has been diagnosed as having multiple sclerosis – to say, yes, we have thought seriously about that promise 'in sickness and in health' and have some idea of what it means. Certainly when we were married we had not, and really could not, give full consideration to its implications in the light of what was subsequently to happen. We did, however, believe that our love for each other was neither infatuation nor selfishly conceived in terms of what each could get from the relationship. Neither of those sentiments could be said to be love as it is conceived in the Christian context where it is concerned for the greater good of the beloved.

In the event that conception of love is tested severely when one partner is afflicted by chronic, intense pain – for if one suffers the other inevitably suffers too. John Donne's words, with which this 'Afterword' began, recall this, so do the words of his contemporary, Bishop Lancelot Andrewes, in a sermon preached on Good Friday, 1597. Commenting on the fulfilment of the words of the prophet Simeon, spoken on the occasion of the presentation of the infant Jesus in the Temple, 'a sword will pierce your own heart' (Luke 2.35), as Mary saw the crucifixion of her son; the Bishop wrote, 'compassion is but passion at rebound.'[5]

I do not suffer what Jenny suffers, but I suffer with her: that is inevitable and inescapable. To pretend that it could be otherwise and that the marriage could be that implied by becoming 'one flesh' would be to labour under a delusion. There are times when I would rather not know; there are times when Jenny would rather not tell me what the current state of batting, the 'pain-score', is, but generally that information needs to be shared if the promises made that day in 1968 are to be a present reality:

> to have and to hold
> from this day forward;
> . . . in sickness and in health,
> to love and to cherish,
> till death do us part

'. . . these three remain . . .'

In the place of testing the Apostle Paul's 'most excellent way' (1 Corinthians 12.31) becomes the only way:

And now these three remain:
faith, hope and love.
But the greatest of these is love.
. . . Love . . . always protects, always trusts, always hopes, always perseveres
Love never fails.

(1 Corinthians 13.13, 7, 8)

I know that there have been times when my love has been inadequate; when I would rather I didn't have to know the level of pain Jenny has had to endure; when my faith has been weak – and 'WHY?' has been a looming and unanswerable question; when my hope has dimmed and it seemed that there was no way forward. But I know that the way of love led one man to a cross and to a cry of desperation, 'My God, my God, why have you forsaken me?' (Matthew 27.46) that was but the prelude to victory. Whatever we may experience in the crumbling of faith and the extinction of hope Christ has been there – and further – before us. Through his Spirit he will be with us and will restore us, if we will let him, in our faith and hope and love.

Come, my Way, my Truth, my Life:
Such a Way, as gives us breath:
Such a Truth, as ends all strife:
Such a Life, as killeth death.

Come, my Light, my Feast, my Strength:
Such a Light, as shows a feast:
Such a Feast, as mends in length:
Such a Strength, as makes his guest.

Come, my Joy, my Love, my Heart:
Such a Joy, as none can move:
Such a Love, as none can part:
Such a Heart, as joys in love.[6]

Notes

Introduction

1 Jane Grayshon, *Pathway through Pain* (Kingsway 1987)

2 Margaret Spufford, *Celebration* (Fount 1989)

2 *Christians' response*

1 Ivan Illich, *Medical Nemesis: the expropriation of health* (Calder and Boyars 1975)

2 Jennifer Rees Larcombe, *Unexpected Healing* (Hodder and Stoughton 1991)

3 *My response: Responsibilty*

1 T.S. Eliot, 'The Love Song of J. Alfred Prufrock' in *Collected Poems 1909–1962* (Faber 1963)

4 *Towards healing, wholeness and growth*

1 Stephen Pattison, *Alive and Kicking* (SCM Press 1989)

2 The Order for the Visitation of the Sick from The Book of Common Prayer (1662). The rights in this are vested in the Crown in perpetuity within the United Kingdom, and extracts are reproduced by permission of the Crown's patentee, Cambridge University Press.

3 The Order for Holy Communion Rite A from *The Alternative Service Book 1980* which is copyright © The Central Board of Finance of the Church of England. Extracts are reproduced with permission.

5 *Reflections*

1 See Introduction, note 2 above

2 Henri Nouwen, *Compassion* (Darton, Longman and Todd 1982)

3 Muriel Green, 'Within the Stillness – Love', 30 December 1990. Reproduced by kind permission of the poet.

4 Joyce Huggett, *Listening to God* (Hodder and Stoughton 1986)
5 See Introduction, notes 1 and 2 above

Conclusion

1 By a sister of Malling Abbey

Afterword

1 John Donne, 'Devotions upon Emergent Occasions XVII' in *Complete Poetry and Selected Prose* (Nonesuch Press 1972)
2 The Marriage Service from *The Alternative Service Book 1980* © The Central Board of Finance of the Church of England
3 *ibid*
4 *ibid*
5 Lancelot Andrewes, 'Now is my soul troubled' from a sermon preached on Good Friday 1597, quoted in *From the Fathers to the Churches* (Collins 1983)
6 George Herbert, 'The Call' from *The Works of George Herbert* (Oxford University Press 1941)

Also published by

TRIANGLE

LIVING WITH ANGER

by Myra Chave-Jones

Takes a positive view of anger and how it can be used as an important part of our lives.

HOW MANY TIMES CAN YOU SAY GOODBYE?

Living with bereavement

by Jennifer Pardoe

A down-to earth look at grief, with many everyday stories to give practical insights into what can be done to understand and help in times of bereavement.

LOSING AND LIVING

Thoughts on every kind of grieving

by David M Owen

Considers a range of personal losses – from bereavement of family and friends in death to the loss of our own health, youth or job. It includes many apt and revealing quotations which speak directly of the experience of grief.

Books
can be obtained from
all good bookshops.
In case of difficulty,
or for a complete list of our books
contact:
SPCK Mail Order
36 Steep Hill
Lincoln
LN2 1LU
(tel: 0522 527 486)